THE CHILDREN'S BELLS

This collection of poems, now brought to-
gether for the first time, has been made by
Eleanor Farjeon from many of her previous
books of prose and verse for children

New York
Henry Z. Walck, Incorporated
1960

THE CHILDREN'S BELLS

A SELECTION OF POEMS BY

Eleanor Farjeon

Illustrated by

PEGGY FORTNUM

First American edition 1960

© Eleanor Farjeon 1960
Printed in the United States of America
Library of Congress Catalog Card Number: 60-6484

To Sally
whom I love

The Children's Bells

(When the half-muffled City Bells rang in commemoration of the Bell-ringers who fell in the First World War, the bells of St Clement Danes could not take part owing to damage.)

Where are your Oranges?
Where are your Lemons?
What, are you silent now,
Bells of St Clement's?
You, of all bells that rang
Once in old London,
You, of all bells that sang,
Utterly undone?
You whom all children know
Ere they know letters,
Making Big Ben himself
Call you his betters?
Where are your lovely tones
Fruitful and mellow,
Full-flavoured orange-gold,
Clear lemon-yellow?
Ring again, sing again,
Bells of St Clement's!
Call as you swing again,
'Oranges! Lemons!'
Fatherless children
Are listening near you—
Sing for the children,
The fathers will hear you.

Contents

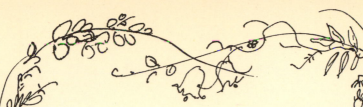

ALL THE WAY

TO

ALFRISTON

All the Way to Alfriston

All the way to Alfriston,
From Chichester to Alfriston,
I went along the running Downs
High above the patchwork plain,
Fantastical as Joseph's coat
With coloured squares of grass and grain,
Earthen russets, duns, and browns,
Charlock-yellow, clover-green,
Reddening wheat and silvery oat:
And rivers coiling in between,
And roofs of little peopled towns.

I heard the wind among the leaves
And corn that was not yet in sheaves
Swishing with the sound of surf;
I heard the cry of distant trains,
The rush and drip of scudding rains,
I heard my foot-beat on the turf,
The lark's delight, the pewit's plaint,
Hoarse calls of shepherds, bark and bleat,
Sheep-bells and church-bells in the heat,
And rambling thunders, far and faint:
And I saw dew-ponds round as pearls,
And multitudes of summer flowers,
Mulleins tall as little girls,
And Canterbury Bells in showers,
Fields flushed with sainfoin, banks that blazed
With golden toad-flax and such fires
Of poppy that I was amazed;
And chicory as blue as heaven
Seen in clear water: I saw spires,

3

And thatches, castles, barns, and towers,
The furnace of a clinking forge
And bridges made of wood and stone;
And by an ancient hostel even
Saw demons in the open street,
A rabbit at a Bishop's feet,
Angels and dragons and Saint George,
When I was come to Alfriston.

I ate my bread on open places,
I changed a smile with many faces,
I loved the jokes and commerce with
The jolly baker and the smith,
The gypsy with her wheedling eyes,
Her pack of wares, her pack of lies;
I loved the rain-storms and the sun,
The silent shepherds young and old,
I loved the cropping, wandering fold,
The silky dog that chased the sheep,
I loved my rest when day was done,
I loved the Downs, awake, asleep,
All the way to Alfriston,
From Chichester to Alfriston.

Canterbury Bells

What are they ringing
And what are they singing,
    The bells in the lane?—
    The dark purple bells

4

In their myriads swinging
    Amid the green dells
    Of the grass in the lane?
'Singleton! Singleton!
Farewell to Singleton,
    Make your farewells!
    But come, come again
To Singleton, Singleton!'
    Sing the sweet bells,
    The wild purple bells
All springing and swinging,
The bells set a-ringing
    By wind in the lane.

Shepherds

You shepherd-boys who spend long hours
Of doing nothing by your sheep
That crop the tiny downland flowers
And the green turf in order keep,

How do you while the time away?
What lonely hills of thought have you
Where you in silence browse and play
Among small flowers and pools of dew?

Or have you all the morning naught
To think about but dinner-time,
When youthful shepherds, sick of thought,
Run down the hills old shepherds climb?

The Gypsy

A Gypsy lives on Kithurst,
    A Gypsy with a dog:
She smokes her pipe inside a barn
    And fills the barn with fog.

The rain came down on Kithurst,
    There never was such rain!
It blurred the outlines of the hills
    And drowned the Sussex plain.

I found the barn on Kithurst
    And peered within the gloom:
I cried aloud for shelter,
    The Gypsy growled 'No room!'

The barn was foul with smells and smoke,
    The barn was full of litter
And blackened with unfriendliness:
    The rain was not so bitter.

The mongrel howled, the Gypsy scowled—
    'No room,' she growled. 'No room!'
I turned about and took the rain,
The kindly rain, the friendly rain:
I took the rain on Kithurst
    And left her to her gloom.

Mr Cooter

Mr Cooter who kneads and bakes
Was sorting currants for his cakes,
And Mr Cooter asked me in
To hear the crickets make their din
    Among his loaves of bread:
There was one dough-cake in a tin—
I wanted that, but with a grin
    He sold me a loaf instead.

We bandied many merry words
While his crickets chirped like birds:
I liked the hot sweet smell of crust,
The currants and the floury dust,
And I liked Mr Cooter too.—
But I smiled my sweetest for his sake,
And he *wouldn't* sell me that doughy cake,
    Whatever I might do.

One Lime

One lime in Alfriston made sweet,
    So sweet, the August night,
That all the air along the street,
The shadowed air in the shadowed street,
    Was swimming in delight.

If any bee had lingered there
    She might have spent her time
In filling combs from that fragrant air,
Her golden combs from the golden air,
    And never seen the lime.

SONGS OF

THE

SAINTS

Saint Joseph

Lo, Mary, look what's here,
My very dear!
It is thy Child I bear
On my two hands with care.
From the small round head
To the small round heels
Thy Babe lies measurèd
Here upon the span
Of my big rough palms,
And needs no other stead.
Like silk his body feels.
What, wilt thou be a Man,
With a man's qualms,
Loves, fears, delights, and sorrows,
When this first night has witnessed many morrows?
Will these feet walk and run?
Will this tongue speak and sing?
And this hand and this other one
Ply chisel, plane, and saw?
How can so small a thing
Fill me with so much awe,
With so much love and wonder
Bow me under?
Lo, Mary, look! thy Son.

Saint Christopher

'Carry me, Ferryman, over the ford.'
'My boat is my back, little boy. Come aboard.
Some men have muscle, and some men have mind,
And my strength is my gift for the good of mankind.'

'Shall I not weigh on you crossing the ford?'
'I've carried a king with his crown and his sword,
A labourer too with his spade and his plough.
What's a mere child to me?   Come along now.'

'Ferryman, why do you pant in the ford?'
'My muscles are iron, my sinews are cord,
But my back with your burden is ready to break,
You double your weight, child, with each step I take!'

'Ferryman, bearer of men o'er the ford,
Christopher, Christopher, I am your Lord.
My frame may be little, and slender my girth,
But they hold all the sorrows and sins of the earth.

'You have borne the whole world on your back through the
    ford,
You have carried a King with His crown and His sword,
A Labourer too with His spade and His plough,
And in one Child all little ones. Put me down now.'

Christopher set the Child down on the sward,
Christopher fell on his face by the ford.
He heard a voice uttering: 'Keep Me in mind!
Our strength is our gift for the good of mankind.'

12

Saint Martin

Sunny Martinmas, you come
When the bees no longer hum
    In the heat,
    Or on sweet
    Summer borders hover.
Then it was so warm, so warm!
Then my lightly-mantled form,
    Bared and hot,
    Wanted not
    Any other cover.

Now it is so chill, so chill!
Hear your beggar, Martin, still!
    Be my stay
    As the grey
    Wintry time grows number.
What sweet charity is spun
When November's mantling sun
    Falls its fold
    On the cold
    In Saint Martin's Summer.

Saint Dorothea

Dorothea to Theophilus: 'I send
Apples of heaven to my earthly friend,
And roses. If your eyes would see them twice,
Meet me, Theophilus, in Paradise.'

Saint Bridget

Saint Bridget she was beautiful
In feature and in deed,
And she would give the world away
To anyone in need.
It was enough for her to know
Of beggars at her door
That women starved, and babes were cold,
And ragged men were poor.

Saint Bridget gave the world away
And cut her golden hair,
To dwell beneath the Holy Oak
Men speak of as Kildare.
The stick she put her lips upon
Broke straightway into flower,
The sunbeam in her greenwood cell
Lingered beyond its hour.

Saint Bridget laid her beauty by
That earth might leave her be,
And God bestowed it twice on her
Till angels leaned to see.
'Look, look! there goes the loveliest one
In Ireland ever known,
Our Bride who gave the world away
And made all heaven her own.'

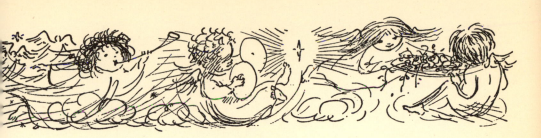

Saint Patrick

A bonnie bairn, my Patrick, the day that he was born!
    (Said the proud Scotch Thistle,
    In her purple and her bristle.)
A lusty babe, my Patrick, when I bore him one fair morn!
    (Said the Rose on her mettle,
    With her thorn and velvet petal.)
Ach! my child wass quick an' cleffer as a changeling-child
      whateffer!
    (Said the strong boastful Leek,
    Who was never very meek.)
Bel et bon toujours, mon enfant, mon amour!
    (Said the Fleur-de-Lis of France,
    That white flag on a lance.)

But the wee triple Shamrock,
    The emerald-green vine,
Said: 'Let who chooses claim him,
    'Twas left to me to name him,
His heart sleeps in Erin
    Wherever I twine,
And by One, Two, and Three
    This Holy One is mine.'

Saint Hubert

Count Hubert hunted in Ardennes
The hart with hound and horn.
So swift he rode he lost his men
Among the Easter thorn.

The music made by horn and hound
Brought none to mend his loss
And share the solitude of sound
And scent he rode across.

Count Hubert chased the noblest stag
That ever drew a pack.
It ran as it would never flag
Along the thorny track.
Sudden, it turned and stood. The young
Count kneeled upon the moss,
For lo! between its antlers hung
The Christ upon the Cross.

The hounds no longer sang their chord,
The horse in silence stayed,
The Figure said, 'Turn to the Lord!'
Count Hubert knelt and prayed.
The stag, on whom the holy day
Had shed a golden gloss,
Serenely turned and moved away
And vanished with the Cross.

Monk Hubert winds no hunting-horn
To wake the wide Ardennes,
He bears no spear as night and morn
He hunts the hearts of men.
With never hound to scent its ways,
Nor horse to stamp and toss,
Hubert pursues the hart whose bays
Bear Christ upon the Cross.

Saint Giles

Underneath the leaves of Nîmes
Giles sat in a golden dream.

Night and morning, to and fro,
Came to him a milk-white doe.

The old Athenian questioned not
Who had led her to his spot,

Why she came, or where she went,
But knew that she was heaven-sent.

*

Underneath the leaves of Nîmes
Giles beheld his white doe gleam,

Giles beheld the arrow wing
Sped by Childebert the King.

Then he heard the King's voice plead:
'Come, for you are he we need.'

The old Athenian rose and went.
Giles was also heaven-sent.

Saint Simeon Stylites

Simeon lived
In heaven's eye
On the top of a pillar
Hard and high.

Men came round
To wonder at him
On the top of his pillar
Gaunt and grim.

They saw his form
Stand up in the air
Like a flame on his pillar
Bleak and bare.

They heard his voice
Like a falling star
From the top of his pillar
Faint and far.

When he died,
Being worn and old
On the top of his pillar
Clean and cold,

Up went his soul,
Down came his bone,
Leaving his pillar
Lank and lone.

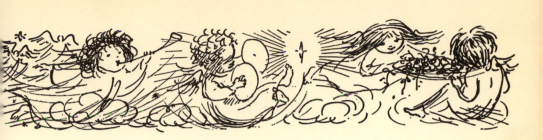

Saint Nicholas

Nicholas, Saint of Children,
Loves to spend his wealth
On pretty toys for girls and boys,
Leaving them by stealth.
The wind in the chimney
Hears children call:
'Bring me this, Saint Nicholas!
Bring me that, Saint Nicholas!
  A silky scarf,
  A bag of sweets,
  A big gold ball!'

Nicholas, Saint of Sailors,
Children of the sea,
When their sails are torn by gales
Close at hand is he.
The wind in the rigging
Hears the sailors cry:
'Save us here, old Nicholas!
Save us there, good Nicholas!
  Saint of Sailors,
  Bring us safe
  Home, high and dry!'

Saint Francis

The kinsmen of Francis
Were not as another's.
The birds were his sisters,
The beasts were his brothers.
These were his names
For the great and the small—
Was not God Father
Of him, and of all?

The night and the morning,
The water, the wind,
The star and the daisy,
Were each of his kind.
God was the Father
Of him and all others,
And flowers were his sisters,
And trees were his brothers.

'Brother, good morrow!'
He said to Friar Sun.
'Sister, good even!'
To Moon the sweet Nun.
'God is our Father,
We know of no other,
And Death is my sister,
And Life is my brother.'

SONGS

OF KINGS

AND

HEROES

The Horses of Achilles

The Horses of Achilles,
With their proud and kingly manes,
They stood beside Patroclus
Upon the Trojan plains.

They stood beside Patroclus
A-weeping for the dead,
Big tears rolled down their faces,
And each Horse bowed his head.

Each Horse bowed his head
To the dusty Trojan plains,
And in the dust lay trailing
Their proud and kingly manes.

King Priam in the Dark Night Went

King Priam in the dark night went
And entered great Achilles' tent.

King Priam in his golden crown
Before Achilles' feet knelt down.

King Priam said: 'The deed is done,
But give me back my own dead son.'

King Priam said: 'Your hands I kiss,
The hands that brought my son to this.'

'And oh, Achilles,' said the King,
'Is it not a sorry thing

'To see a father kiss again
The hands by which his son was slain?'

'King Priam, take away your dead,
And go in peace,' Achilles said.

Queen Dido is Building

Queen Dido is building.
What is she building?
She's building up Carthage so stately and tall.
Who, then, will help her?
Aeneas will help her
To raise the high turrets on Carthage and all.

Queen Dido is weeping.
Why is she weeping?
She's weeping for somebody stately and tall.
Who, then, will hear her?
Aeneas will hear her
As he sails o'er the ocean from Carthage and all.

Argus and Ulysses

Argus was a puppy,
Frisking full of joy.
Ulysses was his master,
Who sailed away to Troy.

Argus on the sea-shore
Watched the ship's white track,
And barked a little puppy-bark
To bring his master back.

Argus was an old dog,
Too grey and tired for tears,
He lay outside the house-door
And watched for twenty years.

When twenty years were ended
Ulysses came from Troy.
Argus wagged an old dog's wag,
And then he died for joy.

King Xerxes and the Sea

King Xerxes saw the sea
Rise up and break his ships.
He tried to hold the sea in chains
And tame the sea with whips.

But when beneath his feet
The long green breakers rolled,
He tried to make the sea his friend,
And gave it gifts of gold.

King Xerxes and his pride
Are dust upon the ground;
No more he cracks his whip and throws
His golden gifts around.

And the sea he could not tame
Or bribe to do his will,
As it flowed three thousand years ago,
Is flowing, flowing still.

Alexander to his Horse

Quiet, my horse, be quiet,
In the sunny meadow!
Shall your great heart riot
For terror of a shadow?

Oh, you are king of horses,
And king of men am I;
And we will take our courses
Together by-and-by.

We two will ride the meadows
Of all the world again—
We will not fight with shadows,
But men, my horse, with men!

The Children of the Wolf

Said old Father Tiber, a-wandering by,
'Two little fish on my river-banks lie.'

Said young Mrs Woodpecker, perched in the tree,
'Two little birds in the bushes I see.'

Said grey Mother Wolf, as she bent down her head,
'Two little cubs that have got to be fed.'

Said the kind old Herdsman, on hearing the noise,
'Romulus! Remus! Two fine little boys!'

When Hannibal Crossed the Alps

Hannibal crossed the Alps!
Hannibal crossed the Alps!
    With his black men,
    His brown men,
    His countrymen,
    His town-men,
With his Gauls, and his Spaniards, his horses and elephants,
Hannibal crossed the Alps!

Hannibal crossed the Alps!
Hannibal crossed the Alps!
    For his bowmen,
    His spear-men,
    His front men,
    His rear men,
His Gauls and his Spaniards, his horses and elephants,
Wanted the Roman scalps!
And *that's* why Hannibal, Hannibal, Hannibal,
Hannibal crossed the Alps!

Caesar's Good Order

Caesar looked over his armies
   And spoke to his legions ten:
'Wash with care and comb your hair,
And mind your step in the Left Wing there,
And keep yourselves in good order!'
   Caesar said to his men.

Caesar looked over the marshlands
   And brought the big roads to birth:
'See they are neat and clean and sweet,
That men may travel with easy feet,
And keep yourself in good order!'
   Caesar said to the earth.

Caesar looked over the Calendar,
   As muddled as any maze.
'Here's winter's moon in the middle of June!
Watch the seasons and change your tune.
And keep the year in good order!'
   Caesar said to the days.

Beowulf the Goth

Grendel came to Heorot,
   The kingliest of halls,
And took his supper on the spot
   Within those golden walls:
On many a Dane he made again
   His meal with lips a-froth—
'But you shall not sup on me, Grendel!'
   Said Beowulf the Goth.

28

Grendel howled in Heorot
  Between the walls of gold,
For the strongest man alive had got
  The monster in his hold.
He caught him tight, as others might
  Have caught a little moth—
'And now your hour is come, Grendel!'
  Said Beowulf the Goth.

Grendel fled from Heorot
  With golden splinters strewn,
But the fair hall stood without a blot
  Before the next night's moon.
Now clear and strong rose sounds of song
  Instead of sounds of wrath—
'For you have supped your last, Grendel!'
  Said Beowulf the Goth.

Bronwen to her Magpie

My pretty bird with plumage black
  And strokes of white upon your wing,
Go fly, and make your airy track
  To Britain and to Bran the King.

Tell him beneath your wing to look,
  Where lies my letter all unseen:
Tell him his sister's now a cook
  Who went from him as Ireland's Queen.

Tell him her sorrow is as dark
  As any feather in your tail:

Tell him she bears the stripes that mark
  Your wing upon her cheek so pale.

Tell him that Britain's Princess, who
  Once gay in Harlech danced and ran,
Weeps day and night for bitter rue:
  And tell him Bronwen waits for Bran.

The Emperors of Rome

There was a Little Island
  Beyond the salty foam—
'We'll have that Little Island!'
  Said the Emperors of Rome.

So this one tried, and that one tried,
  And t'other one went home,
Till at last the Isle was taken
  By the Emperors of Rome.

But as a wet dog shakes itself,
  The Island shook its loam,
Till it had shaken off its back
  The Emperors of Rome.

The Ride of the Huns

Attila rode with his Huns,
The rough and the roving ones.
The folk in the cities crouched under
Their covers, and whispered, 'Here comes the thunder!'

Attila rode with his Huns!
Under the blazing suns,
Under the night's black courses,
Sounded the gallop of Attila's horses.

Attila with his Huns
No longer rides and runs,
And only the stars that were peeping
Remember the place where King Attila's sleeping.

Said Hengist to Horsa

Said Hengist to Horsa, 'I see a white coast.'
Said Horsa to Hengist, 'I see a cocked oast.'

Said Hengist to Horsa, 'I think I smell hops.'
Said Horsa to Hengist, 'And sweet cherry-crops.'

Said Hengist to Horsa, 'We'll pitch there our tent.'
Said Horsa to Hengist, 'And be Kings of Kent!'

Is Arthur Gone to Avalon?

Is Arthur gone
To Avalon
In a black boat, as I hear?
Yes, three tall Queens were there alone
To row and watch and steer.
Who saw him go
And told you so?

His Knight, Sir Bedivere.
Now Arthur's crown is fallen low,
His sword lies in the mere,
    And Arthur's gone
    To Avalon
With a black boat for his bier.

The Gay Young Squires

When Charlemagne went to war
  He left his Squires behind him,
And all the Squires were sore
  Because they had to mind him.
'Although we are not Knights,
  Yet we have Knights for sires,
And our hearts are big for fights!'
  Cried out the gay young Squires.

When Charlemagne went to war
  And fell down in the battle,
The Squires sprang to the fore—
  Oh, how their arms did rattle!
'Our bodies may be small,
  But great are our desires—
At least our hearts are tall!'
  Laughed out the gay young Squires.

32

The King's Cake

King Alfred he could sing a song
    As sweet as any man's:
King Alfred he could fight a throng,
    And think out battle-plans:
King Alfred from his heart so true
    The English Laws could make:
But one thing Alfred couldn't do—
    He couldn't bake a cake.

I'd rather be like Alfred than
    Like any other King;
I'd rather, more than any man,
    Hear Alfred play and sing:
I'd rather keep, for England's sake,
    The laws he made for me—
But I'd rather eat my Mother's cake
    Than Alfred's for my tea.

King Olaf's Gold

When Olaf went a-pirating,
Long before he was a King,
He came ashore and made men pay
Him sums of gold to go away.

But when he came to Scilly's Isle
He stepped ashore and stayed awhile
Among the sunny fields and hills
That were all gold with daffodils.

And from the shore when Olaf went
He still could smell the island scent,
For he bore a gold flower in his coat
And a gold Cross upon his boat.

And Will King Olaf Come Again?

And will King Olaf come again,
Oh, will King Olaf come again?
We saw him leap into the main
And never saw him come again.

The northern sea was red with pain,
The sky had got a crimson stain,
When Olaf fought with Swede and Dane
As no man ever fought again.

Will King Olaf come again?
Will King Olaf come again?
Some say Olaf has been slain,
And some say he will come again.

Norman William

Had I been Norman William
With orchards such as these,
With fields so green and flowery,
With such tall poplar trees,

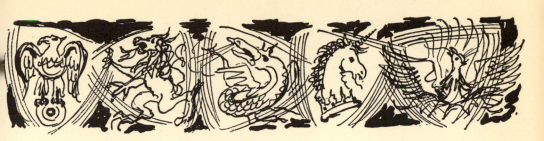

And with the bright broad Seine
  Curling through hill and plain,
The thought of Harold's England would have tempted me in
    vain.

Had I been Norman William,
  Possessing for my goods
Fairy-tale thatched cottages
  And fairy-haunted woods,
I would have passed my days
  Afar from battle-frays,
Drinking sweet apple-cider at the Inn of the Four Ways.

The Hoar Apple Tree

Gold fell the autumn leaf
Over hill and lea
When Harold pitched his camp
By the hoar apple tree.

Gold fell the evening sky
Over land and sea
When Harold fought his last
By the hoar apple tree.

Gold was the Fighting-Man.
Royal gold was he,
That fell when Harold fell
By the hoar apple tree.

35

MARTIN PIPPIN'S

FLOWER

SONGS

The Green Leaf Dances Now

The green leaf dances now,
The green leaf dances now,
The green leaf with its tilted wings
Dances on the bough,
And every rustling air
Says, I've caught you, caught you,
Leaf with tilted wings,
Caught you in a snare!
Whose snare? Spring's,
That bound you to the bough
Where you dance now,
Dance, but cannot fly,
For all your tilted wings
Pointing to the sky:
Where like martins you would dart
But for Spring's delicious art
That caught you to the bough,
Caught, yet left you free
To dance if not to fly—oh, see!
As you are dancing now,
Dancing on the bough,
Dancing on the bough,
Dancing with your tilted wings
On the apple-bough.

What Saw I A-Floating?

A-floating, a-floating, what saw I a-floating?
  Fairy ships rocking with pink sails and white
Smoothly as swans on a river of light
    Saw I a-floating?

No, it was apple-bloom, rosy and fair,
Softly obeying the nod of the air
      I saw a-floating.

A-floating, a-floating, what saw I a-floating?
  White clouds at eventide blown to and fro
Lightly as bubbles the cherubim blow,
      Saw I a-floating?
No, it was pretty girls gowned like a flower
Blown in a ring round their own apple-bower
      I saw a-floating.
Or was it my dream, my dream only—who knows?—
As frail as a snowflake, as flushed as a rose,
      I saw a-floating?
A-floating, a-floating, what saw I a-floating?

Toss Me Your Golden Ball

Toss me your golden ball, laughing maid, lovely maid,
Lovely maid, laughing maid, toss me your ball!
I'll catch it and throw it, and hide it and show it,
And spin it to heaven and not let it fall.
Boy, run away with you!   I will not play with you—
      This is no ball!
We are too old to be playing at ball.

Toss me the golden sun, laughing maid, lovely maid,
Lovely maid, laughing maid, toss me the sun!
I'll wheel it, I'll whirl it, I'll twist it and twirl it
Till cocks crow at midnight and day breaks at one.
Boy, I'll not sport with you! Boy, to be short with you,
      This is no sun!
We are too young to play tricks with the sun.

Toss me your golden toy, laughing maid, lovely maid,
Lovely maid, laughing maid, toss me your toy!
It's all one to me, girl, whatever it be, girl—
So long as it's round that's enough for a boy.
Boy, come and catch it then!—there now! don't snatch it
       then!
      Here comes your toy!
Apples were made for a girl and a boy.

Robin-Run-by-the-Wall

Run by the wall, Robin,
Run by the wall!
You might hear a secret
A lady once let fall.
If you hear her secret
Tell it in my ear,
And I'll whisper you another
For her to overhear.

Jack-Hide-in-the-Hedge

Hide in the hedge, Jack,
Hide in the hedge!
You might catch a letter
Dropped over the edge.
If you catch her letter
Slip it in my hand,
And I'll write another
That she'll understand.

Cuckoo-shoes

Cuckoo-shoes aren't cuckoos' shoes,
   They're shoes which cuckoos never don:
And cuckoo nests aren't cuckoos' nests,
   But other birds' for a moment gone;
And nothing that the cuckoo has
   But he does make a mock upon.

For even when the cuckoo sings,
   He only says what isn't true—
When happy lovers first swore oaths
   An artful cuckoo called and flew,
Yes! and when lovers weep like dew
   The teasing cuckoo laughs Cuckoo!
   What need for tears? Cuckoo, cuckoo!

I Looked Before Me and Behind

I looked before me and behind,
I looked beyond the sun and wind,
Beyond the rainbow and the snow,
And saw a land I used to know.
The floods rolled up to keep me still
A captive on my heavenly hill,
And on their bright and dangerous glass
Was written, Boy, you shall not pass!
I laughed aloud, You shining seas,
I'll run away the day I please!
I am not winged like any plover
Yet I've a way shall take me over,

I am not finned like any bream
Yet I can cross you, lake and stream.
And I my hidden land will find
That lies beyond the sun and wind—
Past drownèd grass and drowning trees
I'll run away the day I please,
I'll run like one whom nothing harms
With my bonny in my arms.

Toad-flax

Toad, toad, old toad,
    What are you spinning?
Seven hanks of yellow flax
    Into snow-white linen.
What will you do with it
    Then, toad, pray?
Make shifts for seven brides
    Against their wedding-day.
Suppose e'er a one of them
    Refuses to be wed?
Then she shall not see the jewel
    I wear in my head.

Shepherd's Purse

If I should be so lucky
As a farthing for to find,
I wouldn't spend the farthing
According to my mind,
But I'd beat it and I'd bend it
And I'd break it into two,

And give one-half to a shepherd
And the other half to you.
And as for both your fortunes,
I'd wish you nothing worse
Than that *your* half and *his* half
Should lie in the Shepherd's Purse.

Queen's Lace

The Queen netted lace
On the first April day,
The Queen wore her lace
In the first week of May,
The Queen soiled her lace
Ere May was out again,
So the Queen washed her lace
In the first June rain.
The Queen bleached her lace
On the first of July,
She spread it in the orchard
And left it there to dry,
But on the first of August
It wasn't in its place
Because my sweetheart picked it up
And hung it o'er her face.
She laughed at me, she blushed at me,
With such a pretty grace,
That I kissed her in September
Through the Queen's own lace.

The Keys of Heaven

She lost the keys of heaven
　　Walking in a shadow,
　　Sighing for her lad O
She lost her keys of heaven.
She saw the boys and girls who flocked
Beyond the gates all barred and locked—
And oh! sighed she, the locks are seven
　　Betwixt me and my lad O,
And I have lost my keys of heaven
　　Walking in a shadow.

She found the keys of heaven
　　All in a May meadow,
　　Singing for her lad O
She found her keys of heaven.
She found them made of cowslip gold
Springing seven-thousand fold—
And oh! sang she, ere fall of even
　　Shall I not be wed O?
For I have found my keys of heaven
　　All in a May meadow.

Lady-slippers

The lady sat in a flood of tears
All of her sweet eyes' shedding.
'Tomorrow, tomorrow the paths of sorrow
Are the paths that I'll be treading.'

So she sent her lass for her slippers of black,
But the careless lass came running back
    With slippers as bright
       As fairy gold
    Or noonday light,
       That were heeled and soled
To dance in at a wedding.

The lady sat in a storm of sighs
Raised by her own heart-searching.
'Tomorrow must I in the churchyard lie
Because love is an urchin.'
So she sent her lass for her sable frock,
But the silly lass brought a silken smock
    So fair to be seen
      With a rosy shade
    And a lavender sheen,
      That was only made
For a bride to come from church in.

Herb-Robert

Good morrow, good morrow, dear Herbman Robert!
Good morrow, sweet sir, good morrow!
Oh, sell me a herb, good Robert, good Robert,
To cure a young maid of her sorrow.

And hath her sorrow a name, sweet sir?
No lovelier name or purer,
With its root in her heart and its flower in her eyes,
Yet sell me a herb shall cure her.

Oh, touch with this rosy herb of spring
Both heart and eyes when she's sleeping,
And joy will come out of her sorrowing,
And laughter out of her weeping.

King's-cup

What shall we drink of when we sup?
What d'ye say to the King's own cup?
    What's the drink?
    What d'ye think?
    Farmer, say!
    Water?
        Nay!
    Wine?
        Ay!
    Red wine?
        Fie!
    White wine?
        No!
    Yellow wine?
        Oh!
    What in fine,
    What wine then?
    The only wine
        That's fit for men
Who drink of the King's Cup when they dine
And that is the Old Brown Barley Wine!
    I'll drink ye high,
    I'll drink ye low,
    Till the stars run dry
    Of their juices oh!

I'll drink ye up,
I'll drink ye down,
Till the old moon's cup
Is cracked all round,
And the pickled sun
Jumps out of his brine,
And you cry Done!
    To the Barley wine.
Come, boy, sup! Come, fill up!
Here's King's own drink for the King's own cup!

Milkmaids

You milkmaids in the hedgerows,
    Get up and milk your kine!
The satin lords and ladies
    Are all dressed up so fine,
But if you do not skim and churn
    How can they dine?
Get up, you idle milkmaids,
    And call in your kine.

You milkmaids in the hedgerows,
    You lazy lovely crew,
Get up and churn the buttercups
    And skim the milkweed, do!
But the milkmaids in their country prints
    And faces washed with dew,
They laughed at lords and ladies
    And sang 'Cuckoo! Cuckoo!'
And if you know their reason
    I'm not so wise as you.

48

Lady's Bedstraw

My lady shan't lie between linen,
My lady shan't lie upon down,
She shall not have blankets to cover her feet
Or a pillow put under her crown:
But my lady shall lie on the sweetest of beds
That ever a lady saw,
For my lady, my beautiful lady,
My lady shall lie upon straw.
 Strew the sweet white straw, he said,
 Strew the straw for my lady's bed—
 Two ells wide from foot to head,
 Strew my lady's bedstraw.

My lady shan't sleep in a castle,
My lady shan't sleep in a hall,
She shall not be sheltered away from the stars
By curtain or casement or wall:
But my lady shall sleep in the grassiest mead
That ever a lady saw,
Where my lady, my beautiful lady,
My lady shall lie upon straw.
 Strew the warm white straw, said he,
 My arms shall all her shelter be,
 Her castle-walls and her own roof-tree—
 Strew my lady's bedstraw.

Traveller's Joy

I saw an Old Man by the wayside
Sit down with his crutch to rest,
Like the smoke of an angry kettle
Was the beard puffed over his breast.

But when I tugged at the Old Man's beard
He turned to a beardless boy,
And the boy and myself went travelling,
Travelling wild with joy,

With eyes that twinkled and hearts that danced
And feet that skipped as they ran—
Now welcome, you blithe young Traveller!
And fare you well, Old Man!

YOUNG FOLK AND OLD

Joan's Corner

Joan has a corner in a garden,
    The garden I am fondest of,
And of all the corners in the garden
    Hers is the one I love.

I'd rather play in Joan's Corner
    Than in the golden nurseries
Where Princes and Princesses sit
    And never make mud pies.

The Shell
(*A Lullaby*)

Am I thy ocean, pretty babe,
That lies against my moving breast?
Am I thy currents and thy tides,
Thy waves, thy rest?—
But like the shell through which my ear
Once drank up all the distant sea,
Thou next my listening heart
The frail shell art
Through which I hear
All heaven, that sent one wave to bear me thee.

Hers

When Joan, aged ten, just after tea,
Thinking of anything but me
(Who stand and watch her from the door),
Sprawls all her length upon the floor,
Turning the pages of her book:

And when she gives an upward look,
Sees me, and leaps into the air,
And, taken with pleasure unaware,
Clasps me: and when with eyes that shine
She cries, 'Till bedtime are you *Mine*?'
And then, all sentiment flung away,
Demands, 'Let's see, what shall we play?'—
Ah, then, I know that of the plenty
To whom she will give joy at twenty,
No other heart will ever know
A quicker joy, a livelier glow
Than mine, who am Hers for play and laughter
Till bedtime, and for ever after.

A Child's Treasure

She has bought, for fourpence, a purse of mother-o'-pearl,
Shaped like a heart, and painted with bright blue flowers,
Cracked, but a priceless treasure to one small girl—
What greater treasure can any of us call ours?

In lovers of gems or pictures more wondering joy
I never saw than the joy that began to leap
In the eyes and voice of the child with the broken toy,
Which, because it was broken—a *little*—she got so cheap!

The Other Child

When I put her in the swing
And set it going while I sing,
And all the apple-leaves of June
Shake in keeping with my tune,

And she cries merrily, sweet and shrill,
'Higher, higher, higher still!'—
Seated on an apple-limb,
Invisible as air,
Watching this child bird-like skim
The speckled world of shade and sun,
Another child is there.

And every time my song is done,
This one, with her innocent brow
And blue eyes almost clear of fun,
Says, It is her turn now!
Lift me down and put her in,
And *I'll* sit on the apple-tree—
And then once over I begin
My song to sing
And rock the swing,
Where only I and this child see
Flying through the speckled air
The other child who's always there.

To Susanna, Reading

Susanna, in your bedtime gown,
One year and three days old,
When I behold you and your crown
Of soft and bleachy gold,
Conning your book with look intense,
And with unconscious care
Reading in words that have no sense
A tale that isn't there—
I'd hoard your precious infancy
For ever like a miser,
For ah! one day you'll older be,
But never will be wiser.

Jessica Dances

When Joy and Molly on the lawn
Danced bare of foot like sprites of dawn
Jessica watched in wonderment
Until delight would not be pent,
And shoe and sock she cast in mirth
And felt her naked toes touch earth.
Swiftly the fresh green joy shot in
Through the fresh young rosy skin,
And in a golden glee the child
Went dancing innocently-wild
Up and down and round and round
Like daisies covering the ground,
Called sunward by the age-long spell
No ages can destroy
Of youth that never sighed or sinned—
While elfin Molly and fairy Joy
Danced on like lilies in a dell
Or harebells in the wind.

Summer Offering

Beatrice with her freckled face
        And her gentle smile,
Kathy, with her head held down,
        But eyeing me the while,
Edie with her ready laugh
        For everything I say,
Knock on my door and bring me flowers
        Every other day.

Moon-faced daisies from the fields,
　　Campions and poppies,
Honeysuckle from the hedge,
　　　Foxgloves from the coppice,
Wild-rose pink and burnet cream,
　　Lady-slippers gold,
They bring me more of all of these
　　Than my house can hold.

I put them in my bowls and jars,
　　My basins and my jugs,
My cups are full of campions,
　　　There's poppies in my mugs;
Sweet Edie, Kate, and Beatrice,
　　A truce to summer posies!
I cannot wash for foxgloves now,
　　I cannot drink for roses.

Bronwen of the Flowers

Bronwen gathered wild-flowers
Up-and-down the lane;
Her gathering touch upon them
Sweeter was than rain.

Now a blossom overblown,
Now a bud begun—
Her eye that lightened on them
Was quicker than the sun.

One by one she named them,
Oh, she did express

In her pretty namings
All their prettiness:

Some were fit for virgins,
Some for merry dames,
And the love with which she named them
Was lovelier than their names.

Myfanwy among the Leaves

Dying leaf and dead leaf,
Yellow leaf and red leaf
And white-backed beam,
Lay along the woodland road
As quiet as a dream.

Summer was over,
The year had lost her lover,
Spent with her grief
All along the woodland road
Leaf fell on leaf.

Then came a shuffling,
Such a happy ruffling
Of the dried sweet
Surf of leaves upon the road
Round a baby's feet.

Year-old leaf ran after
Three-year-old laughter,
Danced through the air
As she caught them from the road
And flung them anywhere.

Old leaf and cold leaf,
Brown leaf and gold leaf
And white-backed beam,
Followed down the woodland road
Myfanwy in a dream.

The Yew-tree
(A Lullaby)

The Yew-tree in the churchyard,
With its black-chambered boughs,
Is as dark and as quiet
As sleep's own house.
But a thousand tiny globes
Are set along its boughs
Like the lamps of the dreams
That light sleep's house.
They are dim as light remembered,
They are sealed on the boughs,
But they're bright as the Grail
To the sleepers in the house.

Château de Chinon

A King once lived, a thousand years ago,
In the great ruined castle on the hill.
Now in the ruins running to and fro
A little barefoot boy is living still.

His granny takes your pennies at the gate,
And in the guard-room keeps her little fire;
But in the grass-grown court he lies in wait
Lest you his pretty company desire.

He slips his hand in yours, and leads you through
The crumbling towers that once were built for wars,
The roofless towers now free to sun and dew,
Whose very dungeons are half out-of-doors.

All those deserted airy rooms he owns,
He feeds his pets where soldiers munched and quaffed,
Careless he climbs the crazy staircase-stones,
And plays in halls where monarchs frowned and laughed;

And in the chapel where a night-long prayed
The peasant-girl whose visions saved her France,
He chatters to you of the holy maid,
With elf and angel mingled in his glance.

Where swords once flashed he throws his paper dart,
Where oaths once rang his little voice runs sweet,
And when you go, no kings tread in your heart,
Only a little peasant-boy's bare feet.

Ball with Yvonne

Yvonne's a little Norman wench
Who knows less English than I French;
But when she tosses me her ball
We understand the game and all.

Yvonne beside the mallows stands,
I catch her plaything in my hands,
I hear her gay approving call—
We understand the game and all.

And when she throws the ball too high,
And, laughing still more merrily,
Sees how I leap and let it fall—
We understand the game and all.

My little brown-eyed fair Yvonne,
In seven years, when I am gone,
To other boys you'll throw your ball—
They'll understand the game and all!

Geneviève

'You say there are fairies in England, sir?'
Said Geneviève, thirteen, and grave.
'Yes, Geneviève,' I answered her.
'Et vous croyez?' 'Mais oui, je crois!'
'C'est pas possible,' said Geneviève.

'Do you believe in God?' said she.
'Yes, Geneviève'—and growing brave,

'Do *you* believe in God?' 'Eh oui—
Eh oui, je crois . . . un peu je crois . . .
C'est mon devoir,' said Geneviève.

The Girl with the Ball

She ran with her ball in her light dress floating and free,
Tossing it, tossing it up in the evening light,
She ran with her ball at the edge of the outgoing sea
On sand which the dropping sun turned bright.

Over the sea hung birds more white than the skin
Of the last few swimmers who took the waves with their
   breasts;
The birds dipped straight as her ball when a silver fin
Glanced in the shallow crests.

She ran so swift, and suddenly stopped as swift
To look at a shell, or splash up a pool in rain;
Wind blew, and she in the wind began to drift
Foam-like, and suddenly ran again.

Children who played on the shore in the last of the day
Paused and watched in wonder her rise and fall
Like elders watching a child: she was younger than they
As she ran by the sea with her ball.

Her hair was loose and she had no shoes on her feet,
And her image ran under her feet on the wet gold shore,
She threw up her ball and she caught it, and once laughed
   sweet
As though the world had never heard laughter before.

At a Window

At an open window
In a small white house
I saw a little bent head
Quiet as a mouse;
A cap of snow-white linen
Covered all its hair—
I thought it was a baby
Sitting up there.

The little figure turned
Its face, so white to see;
It was an old, old woman
Looking out on me.
Ninety were the years
That had worn her white and spare—
I must have seemed a young thing
Standing down there.

I looked up.
She looked down.
Then she raised a thin white arm
Over her white crown,
And waved very softly
Her hand in the air
Like a welcome and a leave-taking
To me out there.

The True Tale of Eliza Ottley

Eliza Ottley, seventy-five,
In Windsor all her life did thrive.
Her father once had mended chairs
And woven baskets for the wares
Of livelihood. When he was dead
Eliza also earned her bread
By plaiting rush and weaving cane.
No poor one asked her alms in vain,
Her only penny she would give
That others, like herself, might live,
For the big cloak she wore kept warm
Her ageless heart and ageing form.
She dwelt alone, but loved the words
And ways of children and of birds—
Much lore she read by hook or crook,
And Shakespeare was her favourite book—
So, rich in nature, poor in wealth,
She reached old age in perfect health.

One day when it was wet and wild,
She met a poor soul with a child.
Swift her big cloak she had undone
To wrap around the little one,
And, getting wet, at last took cold,
Died, and was given to the mould.

This is the tale of one plain life.
Never a mother or a wife,
Eliza Ottley, seventy-five,
Died that another's child might live.
Mother of Jesus, lay your blue
Cloak round her when she comes to you.

A Garland for Agatha Blyth

Here hangs a garland
On a cleft stick,
The four winds of heaven
Round it are met;
When time has withered
The flower that was quick,
The four winds of heaven
Shall sing of it yet:
    Windyfield! Windyfield!
    Never forget.

Here dwells a woman,
Agatha Blyth,
The four winds of heaven
Blow round her cot;
When time has reaped her,
A flower for his scythe,
The four winds of heaven
Shall sing on the spot:
    Agatha! Agatha!
    Never forget.

The Beggar

A beggar with a ragged jacket,
  And battered hat upon his head,
And matches in a little packet,
  Stood on the kerb, and nothing said.
He did not even raise his eye
As on my business I went by.

If he had asked, I might have hurried;
   If he had looked, I might have fled;
But just because he never worried,
   And stood quite still, and nothing said,
I found I could not pass him by.
I gave, and he took, silently.

An Old Man's Epitaph

When I was young I planted thee,
And thou wast younger yet than me.
From every harm I sheltered thee
That might have nipped thy life, my tree.
I fostered thee and cared for thee
When thou wast weaker yet than me.
I passed my prime of life by thee
For thou hadst reached thy prime, my tree.
My time then came to fail by thee
Who wast become more strong than me,
And in my death I turned to thee
Whose years will outlive mine, my tree.
Under the earth I dug for thee
I lay me down—oh shelter me!
That life with which I nurtured thee
Take to thyself at last, my tree.

AN

ALPHABET

OF

MAGIC

A is for Abracadabra

What did I find
As I came into A?
Abracadabra!
(I heard a voice say)
Go through the Alphabet,
A down to Z,
With *Abracadabra*
Behind and ahead.
If you come out of it
As you went in,
As tall and as short,
And as fat and as thin,
Exactly as foolish,
Exactly as wise,
With the same pair of hands
And the same colour eyes,
If you come out of it
Paying no price—
Count yourself lucky,
And don't do it twice!
For *Abracadabra*
May spare a man once,
But he who dares
   Abracadabracadabra
A second time over
Is doomed for a Dunce!

B is for Beanseed

A Beanseed, a Beanseed,
A pink speckled Beanseed,
I'll plant a fat Beanseed in my little plot,
I'll plant it at night
And I'll shut my eyes tight
And sleep until daybreak, and then I'll see What?

A Ladder, a Ladder,
An endless green Ladder,
All tangled with tendrils and red-and-white bloom;
I'll climb up as high
As the top of the sky
By the leaves of my Ladder, and then I'll see Whom?

A Lady, a Lady,
A beautiful Lady,
With a ring on her finger, a crown on her hair;
I'll kneel on my knee
When the Lady I see,
And she'll beckon me onwards, and I shall go Where?

A Castle, a Castle,
A turreted Castle,
With knights in gold armour and gay serving-men,
And I'll live in the air
With the Lady so fair,
Till my Beanseed is withered, and that will be When?

A Beanseed, a Beanseed,
A pink speckled Beanseed!
I planted a Beanseed in my little plot.

The Castle is crumbled,
The Lady she tumbled,
And the Cook pulled the Beans off to put in the pot.

C is for Charms

I met a Strange Woman
With things in her arms.
'What have you got, Woman?'
'Charms,' she said, 'charms.

'I will put one on you
Ere I have done.
Which shall I put on you?'
'None,' I said, 'none!'

Oh how she smiled at me.
'Nay, then, my dear,
Look, do but look at them.
What do you fear?

'I've a black charm for night
And a gold one for noon,
A white charm for winter,
A rose charm for June;

'I've a green charm for woods,
And a blue charm for water,
And a silver for moons
When they're in their first quarter.

'I've a slow charm for growth,
And a swift one for birds,
And a soft one for sleep,
And a sweet one for words.

'I've a long charm for love,
And a strong charm for youth,
And one you can't change
Or destroy, for the truth.

'Sorry's the man, my dear,
Sorry,' she said,
'Who wanders through life
With no charm on his head.'

Oh how she smiled at me.
'Big one or small,
Which shall I put on you?'
'All,' I said, 'all!'

D is for Dragon

There's an apple of gold, an apple of gold
Waiting for you if you're young and bold—
But breathing out fire there's a Dragon, see,
Guarding the fruit of the Apple tree.

There's a Golden Fleece, there's a Golden Fleece
Waiting for you in an Isle of Greece—
But gnashing his teeth there's a Dragon, too,
Guarding the Golden Fleece from you.

There's the King's own Daughter, the King's own Daughter
Waiting for you across the water—
But lashing his tail there's a Dragon, stay!
Lying on guard in Beauty's way.

Oh, if you are for the prize athirst
You must go and vanquish the Dragon first,
And you must not fear and you must not fail,
Or there'll be no end to the Fairy tale.

E is for Elf

Elf! Elf! Elf!
Where have you hidden yourself?
I saw you hanging about,
You might just as well come out.
Where did I see you go?
Under the dockleaf? No.
Behind the water-butt, then?
No, I am wrong again.
Inside the poppy-cup?
Not there! Perhaps wrapped up
In a cobweb on the shelf
Of the gardener's potting-shed.—
Elf! Elf! Elf!
What's that in the marrow-bed?
Bother! But where, then, where?
It's no use hiding yourself
Pretending that you aren't there,
Because I *saw* you, Elf!

F is for Fairy Queen

A lad once walked in Warwick woods
And saw the Fairy Queen.
He dipped his goosequill in the moon
And told what he had seen.

He listened to her roundel-song,
He heard her give the word.
He stole the tongue of Philomel
And sang what he had heard.

Not one lad in a thousand lads
Or in a thousand years
Is given eyes like that lad's eyes
Or ears like that lad's ears.

And long you'll walk in Warwick woods
And search the green-leaved shaw,
And will not hear what that lad heard,
Or see what that lad saw.

But by his song of Philomel
And words of moony sheen,
You'll know that once in Warwick woods
There *was* a Fairy Queen.

G is for Giant

If I were a Giant,
Oh, *if* I were a Giant,
Do you suppose my Uncle Jim would find me so compliant?

74

He'd get that funny feeling
When I glared down from the ceiling
That *I* get when he looks at *me*
If I have been defiant.
I wouldn't go to bed
Whatever Uncle said,
I'd simply swing my spiky club around my middle head,
And tell Eliza, 'Cookie,
I'm feeling hungry, lookee!
So kindly roast my Uncle Jim for supper till he's *dead*.'
And the only one to save him
From the horrid shock I gave him
Would be Me!
Because a Little Boy, and nobody but him,
Can always kill a Giant—
And as I'd *be* the Giant,
There wouldn't be the very slightest hope for Uncle Jim.

H *is for Happily Ever After*

When Brownies filled the milking-pail
And dusted floor and rafter,
The proper end of every tale
Was Happily Ever After.

When Fairies by the baby's cot
Appeared their gifts to waft her,
She lived, whate'er her early lot,
Happily Ever After.

How wise the old tales were, how gay!
Our stories have grown dafter;

They do not always end today
Happily Ever After.

Oh give me back the book again
Whose terrors end in laughter,
And lovers at the end of pain
Live Happily Ever After.

I is for Invisibility

If in some green-shaded woodland bed
You should find the fernseed, child, think well!
Half a pinch of fernseed on your head,
And you will become invisible.

Annabel found fernseed in the wood,
Strewed it on her hair, the old wives tell,
Vanished out of sight, just where she stood.
Annabel! where are you, Annabel?

Someone heard her laughing by his ear,
Laughing with the tinkle of a bell,
Someone felt a tickling grassy spear
On his forehead. Where was Annabel?

Someone heard her sighing in his ear,
Sighing as though all things were not well,
Someone felt the trickle of a tear
On his finger. Where was Annabel?

Child, if in some shaded woodland bed
You should find the fernseed, shun the spell!

If you scatter fernseed on your head
You'll for ever be invisible.

J is for Jinn

If ever in a foreign land
You're going to meet a Jinn,
Keep a bottle close at hand
For to put him in.

You cannot slay him with a sword,
A blow would go right through him,
You cannot bind him with a cord
Because there's nothing to him.

So since you cannot shoot him, or
Garrotte him by the throttle,
Just keep a bottle by you, for
He can't resist the bottle.

When the last bit of him has gone
Inside it, seal it neatly
With the Great Seal of Solomon,
Which does for Jinns completely.

Afterthought

Be sure that there is nothing in
The bottle you keep handy—
It isn't good to mix your Jinn
With lager beer or brandy.

K is for Kobold

The Kobold's a miner
He lives underground,
And when your ear's finer
You may hear the sound
Of the nick of his pick where there's gold to be found.

The Kobold's a miser,
His gold is his care,
And those who are wiser
Will leave him down there
To the click of his pick where there's gold and to spare.

O Kobold, your treasure
I don't envy you!
While I have the pleasure
Of sun, air, and dew
You may stick to your pick, and your gold-pieces, too.

L is for Lorelei

So lovely is the Lorelei
Upon her rock in River Rhine,
That fair young men will gladly die
Only to see her gold hair shine.

So magic is her singing breath
Flowing like River Rhine along,
That bold young men will meet their death
But once to hear her golden song.

78

For no man twice has seen her shine,
And none has heard her singing twice
Where beauty dwells on River Rhine,
And under it, her sacrifice.

M is for Midsummer Eve

Young maids, will you try charms tonight?
The Eve of Midsummer appears.
Nay, if you treasure sense and sight,
   Go to your beds, my dears.

The elder flowers; the unseen crew
Is stirring; do not be too bold.
The young who play with spells may rue
   This night when they are old.

She'll need a charm to fight with charms,
A spell strange spells to put to flight,
An amulet 'gainst magic harms,
   Who magic tries tonight.

Leave incantations still unsaid,
Repeat the prayers that bring no fears;
The Hour is come—to bed, to bed,
   And try no charms, my dears!

N is for Nixie

All in a glance
I saw the Nixie!
It was only a chance,
For her ways are tricksy.
But just where the dance

Of the Millpond waters
Begins, and gurgles and burbles and chatters,
And scatters
Its foam and its rainbow spray
Before it goes rushing
And gushing
Its way—
I saw the Nixie at play
Today.
She was laughing, and lifting
Her arms to her hair,
She was drifting
About in the waters there
Like a white pond-lily
Torn from its stalk,
And before we could even talk,
Willy-nilly
The sliding current
That drives the torrent
Seemed to push on
Behind her—and oh!
I saw her go
Over the cushion
Of glassy water that falls below.
Long, long, long I watched the dance
Of the waterfall, but I watched in vain—
The wonderful moment came never again
When I saw the Nixie all in a glance.

O is for Once Upon a Time

Once Upon a Time,
Once Upon a Time!
Everything that happened, happened
Once Upon a Time!

Lovely ladies wed with beasts,
Tablecloths provided feasts
    When addressed in rhyme,
Magic fish could not refuse
Anything you cared to choose,
Kitchenmaids wore crystal shoes,
    Once Upon a Time!

Little girls in scarlet hoods
Talked with wolves and things in woods,
    Bullfrogs in the slime
Lived enchanted in their fen
Till Kings' Daughters stooped again,
Kissed, and changed them into men,
    Once Upon a Time!

Once Upon a Time,
Once Upon a Time!
Younger Sons were in their glory,
And the end of every story
    Was a wedding chime;
Girls made ladders of their tresses,
Magic nuts held fairy dresses,
Princes wed the right Princesses,
    Once Upon a Time!

What has happened? Nothing happens!
   Life is past its prime,
Everything that happened, happened
   Once Upon a Time.

P is for Philtre

Give me a Philtre, a Philtre!
What Philtre, say?
One that shall make me see Elfland!
Then you must pay.
What must I pay for that Philtre?
A mote from your eye.
Take it, and give me the Philtre!
First say good-bye.
What thing must I say good-bye to?
The world in its dress.
Shall I see Elfland then, when I have stripped the world?
Yes.

Give me a Philtre, a Philtre!
What Philtre, then?
One that shall make the Queen love me.
Pay me again.
What must I pay for that Philtre?
A drop from your heart.
Take it, and give me the Philtre!
First you must part.
What is the thing I must part from?
Yourself, and no less.
Will the Queen love me then, when I have lost myself?
Yes.

Q is for Quest

Wilt thou go a Quest?
That will I indeed,
North, South, East, or West,
According to the need.

What Quest wilt thou go?
That's as shall befall,
And as winds shall blow,
According to the call.

If to her sad cost
Some fair maid is bound;
If some jewel is lost
That must soon be found;

If some evil blight
Lies upon a land,
Waiting till some knight
Strikes with heart and hand;

If some unsolved rune
Brows of sages knits,
Waiting till some loon
Solve it by his wits:

So it only ask
Some part of man's best,
That shall be the task
I will make my Quest.

Art thou the Youngest Son?
That am I indeed.
Go. The Quest is won.
The Youngest shall succeed.

R *is for Robin Goodfellow*

Robin Goodfellow, come home!
England made you of her loam,
In the English roots you grew,
In the English wind you blew,
Never English hearth was lit
But you were a part of it.

Robin Goodfellow, come home!
England's woods were yours to roam,
Not a flower in England sprang
But you teased it, never sang
English blackbird, thrush, or wren
But you took the tune again.

Robin Goodfellow, come home!
Come and suck the honeycomb,
Curdle pans of dairy cream,
Nip the idle maids that dream,
Tip the cronies off their stools,
And chuckle at us all for fools.

Lob, that once upon the mat
Lay in firelight like a cat,
Puck, that once with errant light
Led our steps astray at night,

Spirit of our English loam,
Robin Goodfellow, come home!

S is for Sandman

When twilight creeps upon the land
And drives the sun down inch by inch,
The Sandman with his bag of sand
Comes out to sell a pinch.

Then every child who quiet lies
Pays out the thoughts that stir small brains,
Receiving on his heavy eyes
The Sandman's shining grains.

Powder of coral and of shell,
Crushings of agate and of pearl,
Are what the Sandman has to sell
To every boy and girl.

He gleans the shores of every clime
And bears the world upon his back,
He stores the trickled sands of Time
Within his heavy sack.

Whoever pays out thoughts for dreams
In time and space shall wander far,
And swim in undiscovered streams,
And float upon a star;

And he shall hear an unborn tune
Plucking the harpstrings of the air,

And he shall land upon the moon
And meet old playmates there;

Strange flowers shall blow for him; strange fish
Shall leap in waters bright and blue;
He never shall have had a wish
That might not now come true.

But when the morning comes again
To drive the moon down inch by inch,
Sandman will give him back his brain,
And glean again his pinch.

T is for Talisman

Take this Talisman of me.
Safe you'll go by land and sea,
You shall drink of Circe's wine
And be never turned to swine.
    Warlocks shall not harm you,
    Sirens shall not charm you,
    Goblins shall not heed you,
    Nor lanthorn-lights mislead you.

Take this Talisman of me.
Safe you'll go by wood and lea,
You the Gorgon shall be shown
And be never turned to stone.
    Dragons shall not slay you,
    Trolls shall not waylay you,
    Ghosts shall never fret you,
    And evil shall forget you.

Tell me, you who give it me,
What your Talisman may be?
My Talisman's a chip of wood
Stained with seven drops of blood.
    Ask not Whose the blood is,
    Ask not what the wood is,
    Keep it in your bosom
    And only know what good is.

U is for Unicorn

This is the Song of the Unicorn,
Long ago in India born.
    You know, of course,
    That he looks like a horse,
    His body is white
    As snow in the light,
    His eyes are as blue
    As speedwell in dew,
    And red is his head
    As the fire is red.

This is the Song of the Unicorn,
Long ago in India born.
    You know he was born
    With a single horn,
    White is its base
    As a pierrot's face,
    Its middle is black
    As a raven's back,
    And red is its tip
    As a rose's lip.

This is the Song of the Unicorn,
Long ago in India born.
    So swift was his pace
    That no horse could race
    Beside him. He ran
    Still faster than
    An ostrich. The wind
    He left behind.
    Light couldn't match him,
    Time couldn't snatch him—
So I hope you don't expect *me* to catch him?
This is the end of the Unicorn,
Who was long ago in India born.

V is for Valhalla

Long before your name was spelled
The Old Gods in Valhalla dwelled.

Giants built it in the air
Among the clouds without a stair.

Dwarves in caverns dimly lit
Digged the gold that paid for it.

Then the Gods the rainbow made
That from earth to heaven was laid;

Walking on the rainbow bridge
Trod they to Valhalla's ridge.

Where's Valhalla now? Ah woe!
It was ruined long ago,

And the Old Gods even must
Fall among Valhalla's dust.

Yet if you will watch the sky
Piled with clouds at sunset high

You will see in some great cloud
Traces of that Castle proud,

Walls and turrets, halls and towers:
And when sun still shines through showers

You the rainbow bridge will see
Where the Old Gods used to be,

They who in Valhalla dwelled
Long before your name was spelled.

W is for Witch

I met a wizened woman
As I walked on the heath,
She had an old black bonnet
Her small eyes peeped beneath,
Her garments were so shabby
She couldn't have been rich,
She hobbled with a crutchstick,
And I knew she was a Witch.

She peered at me so slyly
It made my heart feel queer,
She mumbled as she passed me,
But what I couldn't hear.
I smiled at her for answer
And wished her a good day,
She nodded and she chuckled
And she hobbled on her way.

And so I got home safely.
I didn't drop the eggs,
My nose had grown no longer,
My legs were still my legs,
I didn't lose my penny
Or tumble in a ditch—
So mind you smile and say 'Good Day,'
When *you* meet a Witch.

X is for Xoanon

In the days that are long gone
From Heaven fell the Xoanon,
A curious figure made of wood,
A statue primitive and rude.
And fools and wise men gathered all
Together who had seen it fall.

'Behold the magic gift!' one cries.
A second: 'Heaven has sent a prize
Which should by all the world be seen.'
A fool then asks: 'What does it mean?'

The wise men shake their fingers. 'Nay,
Poor fool! that's not for us to say,
Nor yet for you to understand.'
'Well, well! it isn't very grand,'
The fool said: 'Heaven might have sent
A finer gift.' And off he went.

The wise men knit their brows. 'If even
Fools criticize the gifts of Heaven,
We must consider how we well
Can make the gift acceptable.'

So they bought ivory and gold,
And laid the humble wooden mould
With precious plates and scales of white
And yellow, gleaming smooth and bright.
They set it up when all was done,
And cried: 'Behold the Xoanon!'

When men the costly figure saw,
They instantly were struck with awe,
And praised high Heaven for its gift.
And none among them sought to lift
The ornaments and golden crown
Which hid what Heaven had sent down.—

So none the simple form did see
Carved for them from the living tree.

Y is for Yggdrasil

Have you seen Yggdrasil, the Sacred Tree?
Its leaves are in the sky; its roots are three;
It binds with roots and trunk and branches green
Heaven and Hades and the World Between.

Under its root a Serpent coils and clings,
High in its crest an Eagle spreads his wings,
'Twixt root and crest, among the branches green
A little running Squirrel may be seen.

Below the ground a wondrous fountain shoots,
Feeding with magic water the three roots
Of Yggdrasil; and from its branches green
Honeydew drops upon the world between.

Have you seen Yggdrasil, the Sacred Tree?
The eye of man the whole can never see,
By One Eye only Yggdrasil is seen,
With its three roots, high crest, and branches green,
Heaven and Hades and the World Between.

Z is for Zoroaster

How mighty a Wizard
Was old Zoroaster!
The lion and the lizard
Both called him their master.
The sun was his platter,
The earth was his bowl,

The stars didn't matter,
He gobbled them whole,
He skipped with the motion
Of wind for a rope,
His bath was the ocean,
The moon was his soap,
The night was the ink-well
He dipped in to write,
When he wanted to drink well
His wine was the light,
The least sound he uttered
Created a blizzard,
And everything muttered,
'The Word of the Wizard!
Abracadabra
cadabra-cadabra,
Alpha to Omega
Abracadabra,
Look out for disaster!
It's all going faster
And faster, and faster,
And faster
And *faster*!
We're lost in the blizzard
Called up by the Wizard,
The ABRACADABRA
Of old Zoroaster!'

FANCIES

AND

JINGLES

Fairy Gardens

*(In Copenhagen a Memorial Park to Hans Andersen is laid
with the figures of his fairy-tales among the flowers.)*

How many fairy gardens, Hans,
Have you laid out in childhood's heart!
Long since in mine you laid your plans
Which into instant being start
At the first inward look; and there
The Elder-Mother's sitting still,
And, while the Maids-of-Honour stare,
The kissing Swineherd takes his fill,
Karen's red shoes dance through the day
Urged on by supernatural powers,
And with his nuts the small Ib plays,
And little Ida counts her flowers;
There Thumbelina o'er the brim
Of parti-coloured tulips peeps,
And there the little Mermaid swims,
And there the little Matchgirl sleeps;
There children in their myriads call
On Ole Luke-Oie for a tale,
And there, oh loveliest of all,
For ever sings your Nightingale.

Many a child will never see
The Park laid out by Danish men,
Yet of the kingdom still be free
You raised for them, Hans Andersen—
Where, on the magic wind that blows
From Denmark, they shall smell the breath
Even of the World's most Lovely Rose,
And hear the Bird that banished Death.

Pegasus

From the blood of Medusa
Pegasus sprang.
His hoof upon heaven
Like melody rang,
His whinny was sweeter
Than Orpheus' lyre,
The wing on his shoulder
Was brighter than fire.

His tail was a fountain,
His nostrils were caves,
His mane and his forelock
Were musical waves,
He neighed like a trumpet,
He cooed like a dove,
He was stronger than terror
And swifter than love.

He could not be captured,
He could not be bought,
His running was rhythm,
His standing was thought;
With one eye on sorrow
And one eye on mirth,
He galloped in heaven
And gambolled on earth.

And only the poet
With wings to his brain
Can mount him and ride him
Without any rein,

The stallion of heaven,
The steed of the skies,
The horse of the singer
Who sings as he flies.

The Golden Touch

King Midas had the Golden Touch,
It gave King Midas' finger such
Surprising power that if he brushed
A singing-bird its song was hushed,
Imprisoned in a lump of ore
That looked, but was, a bird no more.
The child that in unvalued bloom
Ran to meet him in the room,
At Midas' kiss gleamed hard and cold,
Worth nothing but her price in gold.
The rose he plucked weighed down his hand,
The pear he bit grew solid and
Jarred on his teeth and gave no juice,
What was the use, what *was* the use
To Midas of his Golden Touch?
I do not envy Midas much.

Man's magic fails. But when the God
Of Light from heaven gives a nod,
The bird's brown breast as gold is bright,
And all his singing runs like light;
The bare-limbed children on the shore
Lose their pallor evermore,
Becoming where the Touch doth fall
Like apricots on summer's wall;

The rose among her foliage glows,
And double fragrance from her flows;
The ripe pear glistens in the sun,
And twice as sweet its juices run.
Alas for men who use the power
Of gold on bird, child, fruit, or flower—
Only the gods, who know so much,
Know how to use the Golden Touch.

Neptune

As Pluto ruled the underworld
In shadowed majesty,
And Jupiter the overworld,
Neptune ruled the sea.

His cavalcade across the waves
Was marvellous to view;
His Tritons through the windy caves
Of conches music blew;

Great sea-horses his chariot swept
From oceans chill and grey
To purple seas where dolphins leapt
In showers of rainbow spray;

From pearly shells his Nereids peered,
Old Neptune's laughing girls;
His four winds blew his sea-green beard
Into a million curls;

His breakers, tall as emerald towers
With turrets white as milk,
Sank smooth as meadows strewn with flowers,
And left a sea like silk.

Where sun a golden road did blaze,
And moon a silver made:
Thus upon the ocean-ways
Rolled Neptune's cavalcade.

Seventh Son of Seventh Son

Seventh Son of Seventh Son
Will be fortune's favoured one.
Pain and sickness will not linger
Where he lays his healing finger,
Pennies fallen in the street
Will roll underneath his feet,
And at fairy-time 'tis he
Will the lights of elfdom see.

Seventh Son of Seventh Son
Hath a strand of magic spun
In the woollen of his life.
He will wed a happy wife,
He will know the rainbow's worth
And the secret of the earth,
And a seeing eye will cast
On the future and the past.

Seventh Son of Seventh Son,
Thank your star if you are one.

The Difference

Your eye may see
And your ear may hear
What the eye of a bee
Or a rabbit's ear
Are looking at and listening to
Every day of the year, like you.

But the rabbit's ear
Will never hear more
Than it heard last year
And the year before;
And the honey-bee's eye see no new thing
As it looks on the garden from spring to spring.

But while you grow,
And as you change,
You will come to know
New meanings strange
In the things you listen to, said or sung,
And the things you're looking at now you're young.

That, my dear,
Is one reason why,
With your little ear,
And your little eye,
You are quite unlike the rabbit and bee,
Who never can change what they hear and see.

Fortunes in Tea-cups

Gossips sitting at their brew
Talk of death and birth and marriage:
Who will cross the water, who
Wed a lord and keep her carriage:
     Here's a purse,
     There's a letter,
     Someone's worse,
     Someone's better,
     Dark-eyed stranger
     Telling lies,
     Sudden danger,
     Big surprise,
     Broken heart,
     Storm at sea,
     Sweethearts part—
     Pour the tea!
     Distant friend
     Turning up,
     Journey's end—
     Fill the cup!
Kettle sings and crickets shrill,
Many things for good and ill,
Tea-leaf fortunes false and true,
Swim upon the gossips' brew.

Cats

     Cats sleep
     Anywhere,
     Any table,
     Any chair,

Top of piano,
Window-ledge,
In the middle,
On the edge,
Open drawer,
Empty shoe,
Anybody's
Lap will do,
Fitted in a
Cardboard box,
In the cupboard
With your frocks—
Anywhere!
They don't care!
Cats sleep
Anywhere.

Piecrust

Shall I promise you the moon
And the mermaid's tune?
Or give you a ball
And the blackbird's call?
Shall I promise you the gold
In the rainbow's hold?
Or give you without any
Promise a penny?

More than your prayers
In a promise may be spoken.
Promises are piecrust
Made to be broken.

Plain Philomel

Proud Peacock glitters in the sun,
Plain Philomel is dressed in dun.

Proud Peacock has a jewelled coat,
Plain Philomel a honied throat.

Proud Peacock's song is music's knell.
I will wed plain Philomel.

New Clothes and Old

I rather like New Clothes,
They make me feel so fine,
Yet I am not quite Me,
The Clothes are not quite mine.

I really love Old Clothes,
They make me feel so free,
I know that they are mine,
For I feel just like Me.

What They Do

Cocks crow,
Hens lay.
Cocks know
Break-o'-day,
Hens tell
Break-o'-shell.
Cocks crow,
Hens lay.

Birds of Joy

The Birds of Joy
Shall nest in my hair,
The Birds of Sorrow
Shall not rest there.
O Bird of Sorrow,
Take to wing!
Bird of Joy,
O sit and sing!

The Kindness

The kindness done
To any poor brother
Is done to yourself
More than another.

If a beggar stand
Like a hungry waiter,
Put in his hand.
Your need's the greater.

The Sun that Warms You

Is it not so, brother?
The sun that warms you

              warms me,

The fate that forms me

              forms you,

The irk that frets you

              frets me,

The rain that wets me
                        wets you,
The hour that tries you
                        tries me,
But the sun that dries me
                        dries you.
   It is so, brother.

Low and High

If you are low with humbleness,
   The riches of Christ,
You will give more and say less
   Than the high-priced
Who stalk with empty heart and chin
   Poked up, and give
None of the treasure from within
   By which men live.

What is Time?

   What is Time?
A figment of the mind.
   What is Time?
A nothing and a joke.
   What is Time?
More passing than the wind.
   What is Time?
Less than a puff of smoke.
Time is neither After nor Before,
   Time is—
And is no more.

Presents from Heaven

I will give you
Presents from heaven
If you go byeloo,
Mammy's wee lamb.
I will give you
Seventy-seven
Scales of the Fishes,
Curls of the Ram,
A drink from the Carrier's Water-jar,
The Hunter's Belt, and the Polar Star,
I will give you
Heaven, my heaven,
When you go byeloo,
Mammy's wee lamb.

ROUND THE YEAR

FIRST QUARTER

Aquarius   *Pisces*   *Aries*

January   February   March

A Round for the New Year

Round the ring around
Take each other's hands!
He who pauses in the round
Falls out where he stands.

Take each other's hands
Round around the ring—
Here we stand in winter-time,
Soon we'll stand in spring.

Round around the ring
As we go about,
Old Year pauses where he stands—
Old Year, fall you out!

As we go about
The ground begins to spin—
New Year can the fastest run,
New Year, come you in!

The ground begins to spin,
Spin with the ground,
Take each other's hands again,
Round the ring around!

Aquarius
(*A Zodiac Song*)

An old man with a water-jar
   And beard as white as snow
In heaven moves from star to star
   Spilling his overflow.

As along the channels chill
   Out of the orifice
Aquarius' drops of water spill
   They turn to stars of ice.

Song of the Very Poor
(*From the Old French*)

Old Year is out.
Laugh and make merry!
When you have your heart's desire,
Turn about,
Remember the very
               Poor
Who have no food or fire.

New Year is in.
Eat and be merry!
After you have drunk and fed,
Then begin
To think of the very
               Poor
Who want for meat and bread.

January's Song

I drive boys out
With blithesome shout
On frozen pond
To make their din;
From barren wood
In search of food,
My silver wand
Drives Robin in.
Lo! lo! in by-ways cold
Aconite shows his penny of gold.
Baa! baa! the first lamb bleats,
And nuzzles at the old ewe's teats.

Plow-Monday
(The First Monday after Twelfth-Night)

Turn out for Plow-Monday!
Up, fellows, now!
Buckle the horses
And follow the plough.
Guide the share truly
And slice the square sods,
Wave upon wave of them,
Where the horse plods.
Then the land, ready
And turned, looks its best,
Even more hopeful
Than when it is dressed
Green with the corn-blades
And crop-leaves of May,

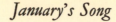

Red with the wheat-sheaf
And gold with the hay.
God bless all fellows
Who buckle to now,
Spending their Plow-Monday
Speeding the plough.

The Running

Oh, the slopes all seemed to run,
And the sunlight ran as well,
Where the small brown deer were running
On the hills of Arundel.

The winds of earth and heaven
Were running low and high,
Where the river ran the valley
And white clouds ran the sky—

And my heart ran like a messenger
With happy news to tell,
While my feet ran with the running deer
On the hills of Arundel.

The Sheepfold

High upon the lonely Down
I came upon a shepherd's town,
A sort of kraal it seemed to be
Within a wattled boundary.
Dividing it, the herd had made
A waving man-high palisade
Of the black-headed rush that grows
Rank on the flats where Arun flows.

Within the outer camp was stored
The sheep's provision, a rude hoard
Of mangolds with their saffron stain,
Heaped near a blue and scarlet wain
Which bore the fairest yellow straw
That ever summer's thrashing saw.
The second closure, littered deep
With that clean gold, confined the sheep,
Some heavy still, some past their throe,
And by these dams the lambs pushed low,
Nuzzling their mothers' dugs; but most
Of those the shepherd yet could boast
Were harboured in the wattle-sheds
Which he had built to keep their beds
From wet and frost. Hard by, his wheeled
Hut stood, and on the open field
Signs of the gypsy life he led;
Less kindly was he housed and fed
Than his own sheep, for whom his plans
Seemed to be nature's more than man's.
Till April he will live up there
With bleating mothers in his care,
The sole wise ruler on that Down
Of his well-ordered little town.
Yet nothing, wattle, straw, or reed,
Or root, that serves his flock at need,
But might have served the earliest sheep
Which on these hills once had their keep;
And nothing does this shepherd know
Or do, not known—how long ago?—
And done, by the first herd whose dams
Upon the high Down dropped their lambs.

The First Lamb

Shepherd, good shepherd, the wind's blowing cold.
What are you doing out there in the fold?
   I hark for a sweet
   And whimpering bleat,
A lamb has been eaned, friend, upon the south wold.

Shepherd, good shepherd, come in from the wet,
The New Year has risen, the Old Year has set.
   Bring the first lamb
   To the fire with her dam,
Though bitter the time be, she'll ean her lambs yet.

The King Rides Forth

King Frost rides forth in Europe
With fist of shining mail:
'This is my hour' (he said) 'of power,
And men shall feel my flail.
I'll turn the rivers into rocks,
I'll seal the water-springs with blocks,
I'll drive the starving wolf-packs down
To prowl for prey about the town—
Yea, I will leave my toll of dead
Behind me where I ride' (he said)
'Even as Attila the Hun
Europe once did overrun,
And freeze with fear the lands where'er
He rode to slay and not to spare.
   Ho, winds, ho!
   Sound an icy blast!

Bitter, bitter blow
As the King rides past,
King Frost who numbs the mountain
And petrifies the vale,
And stuns the tribes of Europe
With his fist of mail!'

Skate and Sled

Frozen are the gutters, frozen are the gardens,
Bitter is the touch of the iron garden-gates,
Ice upon the water thickens now and hardens
For every child in winter who owns a pair of skates.

Snow upon the hill-sides, drifts upon the meadows,
Heaven-sent to boys and girls for riding on the slopes;
Every child in winter who owns a plank or sled owes
Thanks again to Mother Goose for answering his hopes.

Two Young Lambs

Two young lambs
As white as may
Must leave their dams
On Agnes' Day,
And go like little children home
To Saint Agnes' Church in Rome.
There the Pope shall bless them,
There shall men undress them.
When the twain
Go forth again
Leaving their spotlessness behind,
God send the shorn a tempering wind.

Pisces
(*A Zodiac Song*)

I see two fish swim in the sky
    With twinkling tails
    And sparkling scales.
One swims low and t'other swims high,
    Those fishy twins
    With glistening fins.
    But which swims high,
    And which swims low,
    Never ask I,
    For I don't know!

Fair Maid of February

Crocus for Saint Valentine,
Daisy for Saint Margaret,
April-blowing cardamine
    For the Virgin Mary;
But pearlier and earlier
Snowdrop comes at Candlemas,
The innocent our children call
    Fair Maid of February.

Thistles for Saint Barnaby,
Robert's herb and Christopher's,
For the good Saint Augustine
    The bell of Canterbury;
But lowlier and holier,
Snowdrop in your purity,
Ring your bell for Candlemas,
    Fair Maid of February.

Candlemas Day

In the City of Rome
On Candlemas Day
The Pope blesses candles
And gives them away,
Till all, high and low,
Before him have passed,
The Cardinals first
And the Sacristan last.
Then the candles are lighted
So golden and gay,
To the sound of sweet singing
On Candlemas Day.

Good Bishop Valentine

Good Bishop Valentine
Wandered all the night
Seeking out young lovers
And urging them to write:
With bags full of sugar-plums,
Rose and violet bowers,
Hearts, doves, true-love knots,
And lace-paper flowers.

Good Bishop Valentine
By the moon's beam
Went seeking out young maidens
And urging them to dream:
With ribbons for their ringlets,
Love's silken strings,
Orange-blossom posies
And gold wedding-rings.

The London Owl

When in our London gardens
    The brown owl hoots at night,
~~Smutty walls and chimney-stacks~~
    All seem put to flight;

That blackness past the window-pane
    Might hold anything—
Anything wild and natural
    That moves the earth towards Spring,

Anything strange and simple,
    Any untrampled wood,
Or any broken timbered barn
    Where once warm cattle stood,

Any dark hill or reedy marsh,
    Out there when the brown owl calls—
Anything but the chimney-stacks
    And ~~smutty London walls.~~

Abe

(Abraham Lincoln, born 12 February 1809)

Abe he was born in the Backwoods.
    Tough as hickory,
    Rough as thorn,
    In a log cabin
    Abe war born.

Abe he come to Election.
   Straight as the pine,
   Great as the gum,
   Into the White House
   Abe he come.

Abe he spoke for the Black Man.
   White as the birch,
   Right as the oak,
   For the slave's freedom
   Abe he spoke.

Abe he war felled in April.
   Said white birch,
      right oak,
      straight pine,
      great gum,
      tough hickory,
      rough thorn:
'Thar falls the best of us ever born.'

Peep-Primrose

My plot of earth as yet is bare
Of all the bulbs I planted there,
However busy round their roots,
My trees are innocent of shoots.

But by a sooty little stone
Where crouched a bunch of leaves alone,
This morning I stooped down to see,
And oh! Peep-Primrose looked at me.

Aries
(*A Zodiac Song*)

Rampant Ram!
Rumbustious Ram!
Rugged and rampageous Ram!
Romping, ramping,
Rumpling, rambling,
Roistering, rollicking,
Rude, rapacious,
Rough-and-tumble ragamuffin,
Rampant and rumbustious Ram!

March Speaks

Ho-ah! ho!
I crumble the crust!
A peck of my dust
Is worth a king's ransom!
Ho-ah! ho!

Men sow in the dry,
And who but I
Makes the meadowland handsome?
I bark! I bluster! I bellow! I blow!
Harvests give thanks to me!
                    Ho-ah! ho!

March, *You Old Blusterer*

March, you old blusterer,
     What will you bring?
Sunny days, stormy days,
     Under your wing?
No matter which it be,
     You will bring spring.

Whether Lion roaring comes
     Over bleak hills,
Whether Lamb bleating goes
     Seeking sweet rills,
You will bring primroses
     And daffodils.

Whether the earth shows a
     White or green quilt,
Where in both hedge and tree
     Men hear a lilt,
March, you old blusterer,
     Nests will be built.

'Cheep!'

They have found my ledge.
'*Cheep!*' they say, '*cheep!*'
Round the edge
Of the curtain I peep,
Standing quite still
Whenever one comes
To the window-sill
For the new-strewn crumbs.
They fly so light,
They light so quick,
With all their might
Saying '*Cheep!*' as they pick,
'*Cheep! cheep! cheep!*'
In thanks and faith,
While I stand and peep
And hold my breath.

Under My Lean-to

Under the roof of my lean-to,
  The spring in my heart exulting,
I have peeped out and seen two
  Plighted lovers consulting.
      'Shall we build *here*?
      Shall we build *here*?
      Shall we build *here*
      This year,
      My dear?
      Shall we see *here*
      Our comical wee
      Nestlings appear?

124

Shall we, shall we,
Shall we?'
Lovers, decide! decide it!
Ah, if they only mean to
Build their sweet nest and hide it
Under the roof of my lean-to!

First Signs

There are not many blossoms yet,
But in the lanes and banks are set
Sweet in the long wet grass a few
Blue chilly buds of violet;

And the first pushings of the young
Dog Mercury show green among
The black leaves flung to earth when last
The autumn boughs with storms were wrung.

On every slender beechen line
Now in the sun begin to shine
Brown sheaths which still confine the leaf
Within a glossy pointed spine;

And where above the blackberry brake
The trembling golden catkins shake,
Their dotted branches make us know
That now the hazel is awake.

The earth still holds her breath.—But oh!
Soon, soon she will let out that slow
Great exhalation in whose flow
All leaves and buds and blossoms blow.

Pancake Tuesday

Run to Church with a Frying-Pan!
A Kiss for the Woman, a Cake for the Man.

Run to Church with a frying-pan,
  Never you lose a minute!
Run to Church with a frying-pan
  And a yellow pancake in it.
First to carry her pancake there,
  Though heavy or light she beat it,
Must toss her cake to the Bellringer,
  And the Bellringer must eat it.
Then be she madam or be she miss
  All breathless after rushing,
The Bellringer shall give her his kiss
  And never mind her blushing.

A Kiss for the Woman, a Cake for the Man—
Run to Church with a Frying-Pan!

A Morning Song
(*For the First Day of Spring*)

Morning has broken
Like the first morning,
Blackbird has spoken
   Like the first bird.
Praise for the singing!
Praise for the morning!
Praise for them, springing
   From the first Word.

Sweet the rain's new fall
Sunlit from heaven,
Like the first dewfall
   In the first hour.
Praise for the sweetness
Of the wet garden,
Sprung in completeness
   From the first shower.

Mine is the sunlight!
Mine is the morning
Born of the one light
   Eden saw play.
Praise with elation,
Praise every morning
Spring's re-creation
   Of the First Day!

Here's Spring

Here's Spring,
With green on his wing
And blue in his eye:
With a fly
Caught in his hair:
With a fair
Sky for an hour or so:
With a flower or so
For the garden-bed,
And a spread
Of flowers for the meadows:
With lighter shadows
Of clouds flitting over the land:
With more gold for the sand
On the shore:
With more
Music at morning:
With a shower without warning:
With a step lighter
Than snow, a petal whiter
Than frost,
Here's that most
Sweet-footed,
Fleet-footed
Of the four brothers
The young year mothers
Under her wing:
Here's Spring!

Narcissus Fields

The fields are in flower in the West,
The great narcissus fields.
The green grass-wave has a foaming crest,
And the breath of Cornwall yields
A tide of scent that flows
Over the seaweed smell;
'Twixt island and mainland it blows,
Sea-salt and asphodel:

As when, so long ago,
Olaf the Viking rover
Sailed to an isle he did not know,
And the flower breathed like a lover,
Wooing the pagan king
To light on Columba's shore.
The pagan came from the Cornish spring
Christian for evermore.

For the gentleness of the flower
Overwhelms the ocean-crest,
And Christ still walks on the wave this hour
When the fields breathe in the West.

Lady Day

Here's Lady Day.
  Go meekly,
  Think sweetly,
  Talk kindly,
  Look mildly,
  And love your baby
  Like Our Lady
On Lady Day.

March, Blow By!

March, blow by
With your stormy grey eye!
April, run in
With your pear-blossom skin!
  The catkin is shaking
  A powder of gold,
  The daisy is breaking
  A way through the mould,
  The chaffinch is taking
  Her morsel of moss,
  The wind is making
  The rookery toss.
March, good-bye
To your stormy grey eye!
April, begin
With the bloom on your chin!

SECOND QUARTER

Taurus
April

Gemini
May

Cancer
June

Taurus
(*A Zodiac Song*)

Look! a lordly Bull,
Browsing April's grass,
Waiting for Europa
The king's child to pass.
His eye is proud as Jove's,
Godly is his girth,
He bellows for his beauty
Mid the flower-bells of earth.
A garland on his horns
And a posy on his tail,
He'll bear her through the meadows
Like a ship before the gale.

April Fool!

Who will be an April Fool?
Do not fear the jest that tricks,
He who keeps his reason cool
In the rut of winter sticks.
Each one t'other's wit out-matching
In the game of April-catching,
Set for friends your nonsense-snares,
Catch them, and be caught by theirs.
Ere the clock has come to noon,
Be a loon and make a loon.
Do you live by solemn rule?
  Cuckoo!
  Cuckoo!
   April Fool!

A Pointless Tale

Hark to a perfectly pointless tale
That happened last week in a Dorsetshire vale,
    When Nelly,
    And Katey,
    And Peggy the Baby,
Met a very queer fool betwixt sunshine and hail.

Their eyes were like pennies, as round and as brown,
And he asked them their names under Melbury Down.
    'I'm Nelly!'
    'I'm Katey!'
    'She's Peggy the Baby!'
And he gave them three pennies, and went back to town.

Now here's the odd part of this very odd game—
If Nelly, and Katey, and Peggy, by name
    Had been Bessy,
    And Jessy,
    And Tessy the Baby,
This very queer fool would have done just the same!

False April

False April, drest in green,
With cuckoos in her train,
With sunshine and with rain,
    Is here to woo thee.
Ah me! with witching mien
Thy willing heart beguiling,
Now laughing and now smiling,
    Will she undo thee?

Her kisses fly away,
Her yea is turned to nay,
Her love, if not today
  It be forgot,
   Will be tomorrow.
Forget, as she forgets,
This fairest of coquettes—
  Believe her not!
Or trust her to your sorrow.

The Flowering Hills

Oh, flowering hills! oh flowering hills!
See, the wild plums in blossom stand,
And the wind-shaken cherry spills
Her flaky petals on the land.

The swelling countryside has been
Moulded beneath a cloudy mound
Of bloom that hides the dawn of green
And coloured blossoms on the ground.

It will not stay. It cannot stay.
But for a moment from the plain
Rising the sweet year has its way,
And all the hills have flowered again.

The White Blackbirds

Among the stripped and sooty twigs of the wild-cherry tree
Sometimes they flit and swing as though two blossoms of the
    Spring
Had quickened on these bleak October branches suddenly.

They are like fairy birds flown down from skies which no one
    knows,
Their pointed yellow bills are bright as April daffodils,
Their plumy whiteness heavenly as January snows.

Loveliest guests that choose our garden-plot for loitering!
Oh, what a sudden flower of joy is set upon the hour
When in their cherry cages two white blackbirds sit and swing.

A Prayer for Blossoms

The blossom that has started, Lord,
    Protect from this unnatural cold!
The pear-tree has a silver hoard
    Which it desires to turn to gold;
The cherry has her fragile snows
Which later must be warmed to rose.

The trees are eager for their part
    In the world's harvest presently;
On every bough green signals start
    Which lovely fruit in time should be.
Let this young promise, which has cost
The tree such pains be not all lost—
Lord! to the labouring earth send not the frost.

The Cuckoo Comes

This is the day
When cuckoos sing,
And people say
Here comes Spring.
But wise birds stay
With guarding breasts
On Cuckoo-day
To save their nests.

Cuckoo-Come-Again

And are you really come again,
Cuckoo of the one-word song?
    And have you really sounded
    Your blunted note and rounded
    Along an English thicket,
    Adown an English lane?
Then soon the hive will hum again,
And all the gardens come along,
And birds will build their nests for you,
And warm their feather-breasts for you,
    You welcome thief and wicked,
    Cuckoo-Come-Again!

Oh, now the wild white cherry,
The lovely April's very
Loveliest child, will wear
Her silver crown in the air;
And now the small Lent Lily,
The maidens' daffy-dilly,

137

Will blow for every lass
Her golden trump in the grass.
Yes, now a white
And golden world,
Of folded rose, and green uncurled,
And sudden bursts of rainbow light,
And rapid sunny rain,
Will mark the rising of the year,
For she has heard her wakener,
On all her hills, in all her vales,
The forerunner of nightingales,
The double-noted,
Wooden-throated,
Cuckoo-Come-Again!

A Ballad of Palm Sunday

'Twas of a cold Palm Sunday,
Palm Sunday in the morn,
The White Rose of York
Proved the Red Rose's thorn;
The Red Rose of Lancaster
Did bleed upon the snow,
When the Sixth of the Henrys
Was harried to his woe.

'Twas on the Field of Towton,
Of Towton in the north,
The White Rose of York
Against the Red came forth;
By the town of Tadcaster
They fought the hardest fray

Since William of Normandy
Laid Harold on the clay.

Oh Margaret the Queen
Across the border's flown!
Oh the Kingmaker has set
A new King on the throne!
Oh gentle Henry Windsor
Is languishing in thrall!
Oh the White Rose shall flourish
And the Red Rose fall.

Molly Grime

Seven Old Maids
Once on a time
Came of Good Friday
To wash Molly Grime.
The water for washing
Was fetched from Newéll,
And who Molly Grime was
I never heard tell.

Seven Old Maids
Got when they came
Seven new shillings
In charity's name.
God bless the water,
God bless the rhyme,
And God bless the Old Maids
That washed Molly Grime.

Upon an Easter Morning

Upon an Easter Morning,
So early in the day,
The bird raised up his whistle
To tune the night away,
The field raised up its grass-blade
Of emerald anew,
The garden raised its flower,
The river raised its dew.

Upon an Easter Morning,
So early in the day,
The organ in the chancel
Sang both grand and gay,
The people on the causey,
The cattle in the pen,
Heard the pipes of heaven
Rising up again.

The light went like a ladder
From valley-bed to sky,
The lark went like a seraph
Beyond the mortal eye.
The wind went like a spirit
To blow the dust away,
Upon an Easter Morning
So early in the day.

First Catch Your Hare

When does the rent fall due of the Parson's glebe
                              At Coleshill in Warwickshire?
On Easter Monday Morning,
Before the clock in the tower strikes ten
                    At Coleshill in Warwickshire.

What is the rent of the Parson's glebe
                              At Coleshill in Warwickshire?
A calf's head,
A hundred eggs,
And four pence,
Paid down before the clock in the tower strikes ten,
On Easter Monday Morning,
                    At Coleshill in Warwickshire.

Who gets the rent of the Parson's glebe
                              At Coleshill in Warwickshire?
The very first man who catches a hare
And brings it to the Parson's door
For a calf's head,
A hundred eggs,
And four pence,
Before the clock in the tower strikes ten
On Easter Monday Morning,
                    At Coleshill in Warwickshire.

Night-piece

Now independent, beautiful, and proud,
Out of the vanishing body of a cloud
Like its arisen soul the full moon swims
Over the sea, into whose distant brims
Has flowed the last of the light. I am alone.
Even the diving gannet now is flown
From these unpeopled sands. A mist lies cold
Upon the muffled boundaries of the world.
The lovely earth whose silence is so deep
Is folded up in night, but not in sleep.

Gemini

(*A Zodiac Song*)

Gemini-Jiminy, Heavenly Twins,
Castor and Pollux as like as two pins,
Born in an eggshell and borne to the blue,
Jiminy-Gemini, how do you do?

The Next Holiday

Lads and Lasses, up and out!
    You who from your dads of old
Hied away, with ne'er a doubt
    Youth must dance though Age grow cold:
You who pledged yourselves to meet
    One another every May—
By those twelve old kisses sweet,
    This is your Next Holiday!

Is the Maypole not in sight,
  Is the Fiddler's tune unheard,
Yet when May-Day breaks in light
  Still you'll hear a piping bird.
Is the game of cakes and ale
  Played no longer in a bower,
Yet the May-Game will not fail
  Till the meadows cease to flower.

Jane and John, and Hal and Sue,
  Nat and Wat, and all the throng,
Ghosts of Nursery Tale are you?
  Echoes faint of Nursery Song?
No! as long as Lasses laugh,
  And as long as Lads have eyes,
In the street or on the grass,
  Youth will kiss, though Age grow wise.

Still you'll meet beneath the sun
  In your buckled dancing-shoon,
And at night, the dancing done,
  Still you'll part beneath the moon.
Some with sighs, with laughter some,
  Pledged to meet another May—
Sweethearts, leave your dads and come!
  This is your Next Holiday!

Invitation to Bess

Bessie, rise and wash your face,
Hat and gown with ribbons lace,
  For the May,

And to fields of Charing come,
Where the merry fiddles hum
    All the day.

There we'll join the jolly souls
Winding mazes round the poles
    Raised on high,
Where the garland overhead
Swings its yellow, white, and red
  Airily.

In a bower set with green
We will curtsey to the Queen
    As we pass,
In a booth our ease we'll take,
Munching painted ginger-cake
    On the grass.

If we see at even-close
Ladies dance in silken hose
    Drinking wine,
Blowing from our ale the froth
We'll dance gay in hose of cloth
    Half as fine.

Hark! the lusty tabors beat!
Hark! the horns wind, and the sweet
    Gitterns thrum!
Dress yourself against the day,
And with me to fields of May,
    Sweet Bess, come.

May's Song

The moon is on the meadow,
The nightingale awake,
I have no rest within my breast,
So sweet my heart doth ache.
The blackbird in the garden
Is calling like a bell.
Ah cease! or I of joy shall die,
So full my heart doth swell.
The year's green wave has risen
And broken round my feet—
Oh world of flowers! Oh golden hours!
Oh heart, too full, too sweet!

Furry-Dance

The Furry-men in Helston
   To tune of *Hal-on-Tow*
Through the houses of the town
   On May's eighth morning go.
With top-hats on their noddles
   And dress suits on their backs
And lilies in their buttonholes
   The maidens they do tax.
Here a kiss and there a kiss,
   They take their dues, you know,
The day they do the Furry-Dance
   To tune of *Hal-on-Tow*.

Out Came the Sun!

Out came the sun,
And out came the dresses!
Girls every one
From tissue recesses
Pulled out the new frock,
The yellow, the pink,
The lavender-blue frock—
And all in a twink
Each one had got on
Her muslin or cotton,
Going all gay on
Gingham and rayon,
Golden as sunlight,
Clear as the sky,
White as the wisp
Of the cloud floating by;
All clean and crisp
They came in the hour
Of the one light that opens—
The heart of the flower!
Girls in their summer-gowns
Patterned and plain,
   Girls in green dots
    And rose-coloured spots,
Girls like the rainbow that follows the rain
Brightened the streets of the cities again.

Five Trees

(It is said that in fifty years the oak, beech, elm, ash, and sycamore will have almost disappeared from the English forests, because hardwood trees are in less demand than softwood timber.)

How lovely in the English wood,
　　And on the English mead,
These five among our trees have stood
　　To serve the country's need.
Must they, like yeoman stock of yore,
　　Pass from the rustic realm,
The beech, the oak, the sycamore,
　　The ash-tree, and the elm?

These have been rafters of our roof,
　　Upholders of our walls,
These have made wind and weather-proof
　　Our granaries and stalls;
The plough, the wagon, and the yoke,
　　The arrow's airy flash,
Came from the sycamore and oak,
　　And elm and beech and ash.

On us their spreading arms have shed
　　Green shadow like a grace;
Us they have served as board and bed
　　And the last resting-place;
Now must they drop their ancient store
　　Somewhere beyond our reach,
The oak, the ash, the sycamore,
　　The elm-tree, and the beech?

Blue Magic

In the woods the bluebells seem
Like a blue and magic dream,
Blue water, light and air
    Flow among them there.

But the eager girl who pulls
Bluebells up in basketfuls
When she gets them home will find
    The magic left behind.

Spring Night in a Village

The hot May night is like July,
    Footsteps and passing voices fall
Upon the warm air echoingly
    This evening. In the Village Hall

The boys and girls dance merrily
    To an old piano's jangled tone.
Down in The Bull the laugh runs high,
    And someone starts a gramophone.

And from a small, sweet garden I
    Can see in heaven a perfect moon,
On earth a perfect peony,
    And hear no sound that's out of tune.

The Quest

*(An American ornithologist once travelled 3,000 miles in
order to hear the song of an English nightingale.)*

Three thousand miles to hear a nightingale.
  Oh, the long journey and the lovely quest!
The realms of fable and of fairy tale
  Only can show such ardour: in the breast

Of Orpheus, journeying through Elysium
  To find his love and bear her home to Greece;
Or of the heroes of the Argo, come
  Through leagues of dangers for a Golden Fleece;

Of Phaëton who drove across the sky
  Before he was to death and darkness hurled;
Of the young Queen for whom, lest she should die,
  Men sought the loveliest rose in all the world;

Of Knights who rode on quests which men thought vain,
  For ever following the Holy Grail:
All these revive in us who once again
  Travel the earth to hear a nightingale.

Whatever toils the journey may impose,
  Its end is beauty: the beloved shade
May melt as soon as clasped, the wondrous rose
  May vanish, and the Golden Fleece may fade,

The sun destroy us as we hold the reins,
  The Grail itself be but an instant seen,
The song fall silent:—while we face new pains
  Upon the memory of what has been.

The quest ends never. Men will come along,
  Following us where we succeed and fail,
Spending their lives in labour for a song,
  And crossing worlds to hear our nightingale.

Oak Apple Day

On Oak Apple Day in Wishford
  The Wiltshire wives will go
To gather green oak in Grovely Wood
  With none to say them no.

Around the streets of Wishford
  With branch and bough they'll go,
Borne from the oaks of Grovely Wood
  Where no man said them no.

And the woodcutting rights in Grovely
  Shall never from Wishford go
While the wives get faggots on Oak Apple Day
  With none to say them no.

Kingcups in Town

Down the street the old man came,
And on his head he bore a flame.

I stopped to gaze, so he stopped too.
'Want some?' he said. 'Indeed I do.

Where did you get them?' 'Uxbridge way,
All the lot fresh-picked today

Off the island there,' he said,
Shifting the basket from his head.

'You gets 'em when the water's out,
O' course. I had to wait about

All night for 'em. The bud'll bloom
Lovely when they're in your room.'

I took the bunch from him, still wet,
And then the kingcup-gatherer set

His brimming basket on his old
Grey head, and walked beneath the gold,

Yes, walked off in his broken boots,
And the shabbiest of suits,

Crowned in the may-time of the spring,
More gloriously than a king.

Cancer
(*A Zodiac Song*)

Over the beaches of the sky
The Crab no fisherman has caught
Ambles his clumsy course in June.

The silver shells of stars unsought
By mariners and children lie
About his sidelong journey strewn.

Heaven's bed lies high and dry.
Old Shellback with a single thought
Clambering up the hot blue dune

Sees and thinks and wishes naught
In night's dark aridity
But the clear pool of the moon.

June's Song

I bring you my rose.
It is a golden flame.
Is Love its name?
It is a scarlet fire.
Is it desire?
'Tis the white ash of coal.
Is it the soul?
One, none, or all of those,
I bring you my rose.

May-Day in June

On Shillingstone Green
A Maypole towers.
On June the Ninth
They dress it with flowers,
And do their dance
And sing their tune
And keep May-Day
On the Ninth of June.

The wreaths are left
Until they are brown,
The pole stands up
Until it falls down,
And why these Dorsetshire
Folk do so
Never ask me
For I don't know.

Gold-weed

They called my buttercup a weed
And told me, 'Pull it up!'
I let it stand and flower and seed,
My golden buttercup.

Next year when it was twice its size,
'Root out that weed!' they said.
I let it stand and spread and rise
And seed upon its bed.

In the third year when it came up
My gold-weed was a bower,
And when they saw my buttercup,
They cried out, '*What* a flower!'

THIRD QUARTER

Leo   *Virgo*   *Libra*
July   August   September

Leo
(*A Zodiac Song*)

The Lion with his flaming mane
Burns his way through heaven again.
His voice is thunder in the sky,
And there is lightning in his eye.

Who's that Bleating?

Who's that bleating
Down by river?
Sheep are sweating,
Soon they'll shiver.
Back to farm
Without their wool,
We'll go warm
And they'll go cool.

July's Song

Wash the sheep, and shear the sheep,
    And make my pillow of wool,
Whiles I settle down to sleep
    Besides the washing-pool.
Shear and wash and shear the sheep,
    And drop the fleece again,
Whiles 'tween grass and leaf I sleep
    A-nigh the shearing-pen.

157

Shear and wash, and wash and shear,
  Soft fall the fleece on me,
The heavy dreaming of the year
  In fertility.

Come Down to the Water

Come down to the water,
The water is cool,
The fire of the sun
Is dissolved in the pool,
The dragon-fly hovers,
The water-bugs spin,
Come down to the water,
Young men, and dive in.

Come down to the water!
The water is clear,
The river will chasten
The heat of the year,
The lily has turned back
Her star to the brim,
Come down to the water,
Young maidens, and swim.

Come down to the water!
The water is bright
With the sun in the morning,
The moon in the night.
The shoals of small fishes
Dart startled away,
Come down to the water,
Young children, and play.

Come down to the water!
The water is clean,
In the sun it is blue,
In the shade it is green,
The kingfisher flashes,
The swan spreads her sail,
Come down to the water,
Tired folk, and grow hale.

Come down to the water!
The water is sweet,
It drops a new universe
Under your feet,
Your body below you
Waits naked and fair,
Go down in the water
And meet yourself there.

Saint Swithin's Wish
(July 16)

I'll lie (said Swithin)
Somewhere within
Sound of things
Like birds' wings,
Raindrops' beat,
Insects' feet,
Cows lowing,
Peasants going,
Seeds springing,
People singing,
Boys clattering,
Girls chattering,

Men walking,
Women talking,
Children's tread
(*Swithin said*).
Who shifts the earth wherein I lie
For forty days shall not go dry.

Open Eye, Pimpernel

Open eye, Pimpernel, chin-in-the-dust!
Sun in the heavens is yellow as rust.
Shut your eye, Pimpernel, chin-in-the-dew!
Rain from the heavens is come to drown you.

Remember the Grotto!

A penny, kind lady!
Remember the Grotto!
A penny, kind Gentleman,
All for our motto.
    We build our wee cloister
    With shells of the oyster,
    And somewhere inside
    A candle we hide;
    The little wick flames
    In the name of St James.
But don't ask us why,
For we could not reply,
We ask for a penny
One day in July,
Or what is our motto,
Or why it's a Grotto.

Poppies

Cold reigns the summer, and grey falls the day,
The flame of the year is smouldering away,
But here in the hedgerow and yonder in the wheat
The flame of the poppy is throwing out its heat.

Small grows the corn and scant is the yield
Of the hay lying strewn upon the stubble field,
But there in the meadow and here by the road
The red poppy glows as in other years it glowed.

Sunrise comes chilly and sunset comes wet,
And low burns the flame where the sun rose and set,
But red as the flame of a dawn that will not pass
The fire of the poppy is lighted in the grass.

Virgo
(A Zodiac Song)

Over the hilltop
And over the town
The Virgin goes walking
With stars in her gown,
Stars on her left hand
And stars on her right,
She wakes with the twilight
And walks in the night.

Casabianca
(The Battle of the Nile, 1 August 1798)

Sea, be kind to a young Boy's Bones
Who died in Battle in Afric Zones:
When Nelson fir'd his Father's Ship
They took Together her last Trip

While Others fled the Fiery Breath,
As their Captain lay in Death,
It was this Infant's only Boast
That he would not quit his Post.

Ere Manhood Learn'd on him to smile,
Dyed in the Battle of the Nile
Casabianca *aetat* 10.
Honour him as you would Men.

The Child in the Train

The train stands still
   And the world runs by.
Yonder runs a tree
   And a cloud in the sky.
Here flies a pony
   On the running road,
And there flows the quickest
   River ever flowed.

The mountains on the edge
   Roll away like the tide,

162

The backs of the houses
  Pass on a slide,
The little farms slip off
  As soon as one looks,
And the little churches vanish
  With their spires and their rooks.

The buttercup embankments,
  The telegraph wires,
The names of the stations,
  The small heath fires,
The hoardings in the fields,
  And the people in the street,
Go whizzing into somewhere
  While I keep my seat.

The little cities trot,
  And the little hamlets trip,
The meadow with its cow,
  The sea with its ship,
The forest and the factory,
  The hedge and the hill—
The world goes running by
  While the train stands still!

Loganberry Spooks

You know the four poles in the garden
Where the best of the logans grow?
The birds they're watching of 'em,
For they're ripening fast, you know.

So today my mother she rootled
Among her old white rags,
And 's done up the loganberry poles
In muslin-curtain bags.

But oo! they're looking so queersome!
They've gone such funny shapes
With the bundling up of the crooked poles
In muslin tied with tapes.
One it looks like a hobbling witch,
And one swelled out with wind
Looks like my great-great-grandmother
With her two old maids behind.

When the sun's a-shining
I can laugh at any bird
That longs for logans, and 's frightened
Of anything so absurd.
But when the moon's a-shining,
And white looks more than white,
I wouldn't go near those logan-spooks
A-rearing up in the night—
    Never tell me they're nowt but posts!
    I'll steer clear of the logan-ghosts
    When summer moon shines bright.

Heltery-skeltery

    Run, rabbit, run!
    Run to your warren!

The harvest is done,
The meadow is barren,
The corn was your shelter
From stone, stick, and gun,
Heltery-skeltery
Run, rabbit, run!

The Gleaners

The field is shaven to its stubble,
    The sheaf is borne away,
Yet here the aged folk bent double
    Go stooping through the day,
To glean with hardly counted trouble
    Some corn to bear away.

Whole families, the old grandmother,
    The woman whom she bore,
The tiny sister, tinier brother,
    All search the golden floor
For one more ear, and then another,
    To swell their scanty store.

The ancient bounty plenty granted,
    How long ago, to Ruth,
Granted to these: but oh, how scanted
    Life's bread must be in truth,
When for a handful sorely wanted
    Age stoops all day with youth.

This Bread

This bread,
This bread
That carelessly you crumble,
Was once the red
Wheat, the green oat, the humble
Barley that filled
The dreams of the unfed,
Man, woman, and child.
Respect this holy bread.

Sweet Robin Herrick

(Born 20 August 1591)

This day Robin Herrick
Was born in Cheapside,
His father he laughed
And his mother she cried,
So to sweet Robin Herrick
'Twas given to spy
The tear in the marigold's
Laughing eye.

Hunger-harvest

The hay's long cut,
The corn is in,
The apple-orchard's
Light and thin.

The ricks are thatched,
The barns in store,
The shelves and garrets
Groan once more.

God help the grass
That did not yield,
God help the stricken
Harvest-field.

God help the trees
Pinched by the rime
That killed the fruit
In blossom-time.

God help the folk
That looked to these,
The corn, the clover,
And the trees.

Where apples fail
And wheat is thin
The hunger-harvests
Now begin.

Libra
(*A Zodiac Song*)

The gold scales of heaven
See how they swing
With fruits of the fall
That were flowers in the spring.

Fill the gold scales
With apples and pears,
Seraphim, Cherubim,
Come for your shares.

Weigh the gold scales
With damson and plum,
Come, saints and angels
And archangels, come.

September's Song

In orchard set yer ladders,
    Yer baskets on the ground,
Sort windfalls in the shadders
    Of low-spread boughs around.
Then whoam to kitchen, neighbour,
    Drink deep and sleep you sound!
So let the apple-labour
    In apple-juice be drowned.
        Haw! haw! haw!
Come pass the cider round.

Thieves in the Orchard

The wasps in the orchard
    Are tasting the fruits
Where the apples are strewn
    At the apple-tree roots;
The red and gold apples,
    Half-robbed of their sweet,
Lie bitten and spoiled
    In the grass at my feet.

Look! deep in the orchard,
   And quite on her own,
Tasting this tree and that tree
   Goes little pink Joan—
One bite at each apple
   She fancies, alas!
Then bitten and spoiled
   It is flung in the grass.

Oh, Joan, if I catch you,
   My sweet eight-year-old,
With your lips like a pippin
   And cheek russet-gold,
With your ripening apples
   The wasp I will play—
But leave their full sweet
   For another some day.

Half a Pound of Blackberries

Half a pound of blackberries!
Half a pound of blackberries!
Who will buy my summer prize,
Half a pound of blackberries?

I will give you half a penny,
Sweetheart, take it and be wise—
You'll not get a better offer
For your half-ripe blackberries.

Master, not for half a kingdom
Would I sell my summer prize,
My first-fruits that are but half-fruits,
My half-pound of blackberries.

Half a day I took to gather them,
Half a day as old time flies—
Half a day I have to sell with
Half a pound of blackberries!

Scents of thyme and wild sweet marjoram
From the breathing turf arise—
Will you buy that summer sweetness,
Master, with my blackberries?

There a shimmering world of harebells
With a world of scabious vies—
Will you buy their fairy colours
All along of blackberries?

Silky polls of seeding thistles
Puff their cloudlets to the skies—
Will you buy the thistles' lovelocks
With my early blackberries?

Will you buy my lazy gathering,
My half-laughter, my half-sighs,
Where the sheep have half done browsing
My half-dreams in my half-drowsing?—
Half my heart I left there drowsing
Where the sheep will find it, browsing—
Master, will you buy my lazy
Half a pound of blackberries?

I will make you half an offer—
Sweetheart, will you be half-wise?—
I will give you half a kiss for
Half a pound of blackberries.

Apple-time

Your time is come, you apple-trees,
   Your labours weigh upon the bough,
Your heavy branches ask for ease
   And here we come to ease them now.
In April's hour of bridal bliss
You bloomed for this, you bloomed for this.

All day the lengthy ladders lean
   Their stairs against the twisty trunk;
We mount on them to chambers green,
   And before twilight falls are drunk
As bees upon the heady scent
In which the golden day was spent.

The baskets bear away the yield:
   Dull Russet, glossy Quarrenden,
Green Wellington, and scarlet-peeled
   Pearmain; the arms of girls and men
Ache with the streaked and yellow bales
Of Pippins and small Curlytails.

And some must to the cider-press
   Their juices in the crush to spill,
Some to the larder, some to dress
   The table, some must barrels fill,

And some must to the apple-loft
Whence greedy hands shall steal them oft.

The ruddy apple of the sun,
   The golden apple of the night,
Shall watch our toil till all is done,
   And we grow tired as you grow light.
You apple-trees, give up your sum—
Your time is come, your time is come.

The Favourite Fruit

If you of all the fruits that be
Could choose a fruit to bite,
Which tree would be your favourite tree
At morning, noon, and night?

There's oranges for golden drink,
And cherries for bright toys,
And melons where you almost sink
Your face in mushy joys.

There's plums as purple as the dusk
And clear as yellow moons,
And mangoes that out-sweeten musk,
To eat with silver spoons.

There's gooseberries whose furry coats
Like caterpillars grew,
And currants black as music notes
And bright as drops of dew.

No, none, no, none of mine are these!
Like Adam I was born
To go and seek the apple-trees
By noon and night and morn;

The green, the yellow, and the red,
The streaky pippin-stripe,
The windfall, and the still unshed,
The ripe and the unripe—

If I of all the fruits that be
Can choose which fruit I'll bite,
My favourite tree's the apple-tree
By morning, noon, and night.

A Song for September

Now on the Arun mists rise up like sleep,
    And turn the hosts
Of trees and bushes, hayricks, cows, and sheep,
    To unsubstantial ghosts;

And every night's a white and silver night,
    With the great slow
Round harvest moon shedding her drifts of light,
    Through bodiless drifts of snow;

And every morning, when the swaddled sun,
    In fleeces rolled,
Begins to burn away his garments one
    By one, is white and gold.

173

Through the bright air, sprinkling at every pore
    With diamond rain,
Cattle and hayrick, elm and sycamore
    Take life and body again.

But still all roads and woodsides crouch beneath
    A muffled cloak,
Where Old Man's Beard steals like September's breath,
    And summer's funeral smoke.

Farewell to Summer

Fare you well
in your golden shawl,
loveliest Summertime
of all.

Go your ways
with your deep blue eyes,
your tropic nights,
your Italian skies.

Go your ways
with your glowing skin,
apricot, peach,
and nectarine.

Go your ways
with your gleaming hair,
that burned the wreath
of roses there.

You raised our harvests
before their hour,
scorched the herbage
and forced the flower:

but brought such joys
in your shining train
as we may not know
for years again.

In your glittering nights
and dazzling dawns
you turned our youth
into nymphs and fauns,

enchanting us
with bewildering sweet
rapturous light
and radiant heat.

Dreaming October
turns the page.
Fare you well,
O Golden Age!

Go your ways
in your golden shawl,
loveliest Summertime
of all.

FOURTH QUARTER

Scorpio	*Sagittarius*	*Capricorn*
October	November	December

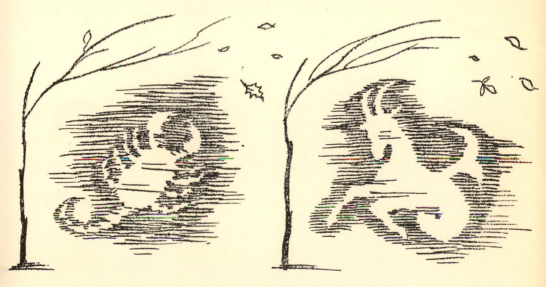

Scorpio
(*A Zodiac Song*)

Scorpion, like a lobster slipped
    Across its reef,
Within his fatal claw has nipped
    The yellow leaf,
He has come to sting the rose
    And blight the grass.
What wonder veiled October goes
    Sighing *Alas*.

October's Song

    The forest's afire!
    The forest's afire!
The maple is burning,
The sycamore's turning,
    The beech is alight!
Make a pyre! make a pyre!
Bring the oak to the fire!
The forest is glowing!
The greenleaf is flowing
    In flame out of sight!

Brothers and Sisters
(*4 October, St Francis' Day*)

Come forth, O beasts! This is the day
   Of that dear Saint who called you brother,
Who greeted you upon the way
   As one companion does another,

And saw in God's creative plan
No difference between beast and man.

Fly down, O birds! This is the day
    Of that sweet Saint who sister named you,
Who, coming in your midst to pray,
    By love, and by love only, tamed you,
And read in the Creator's word
Equal delight for man and bird.

What! not one furry thing runs out?
    What! not a single flying feather?
Men separate with fear and doubt
    What love was wont to bring together.
To bird and beast we call in vain
Till Brother Francis walks again.

A Memory

That October morning
    Had a clear gold sun,
Round the turning trees
    A snow-white mist was spun,
In the quiet river
    The palest sky was seen,
Half the chestnut-fans
    Were yellow, half were green,
Soft were the dreams of autumn,
    Peace lay on the land,
When the fallow deer of Magdalen
    Fed from my hand.

Remembrance

I know the beech has got its red,
   I know the lime has got its gold,
And bracken is a tawny bed,
   And dawn is white with mist, and cold;

I know the beauty of the hedge
   Instead of flowers is berries now,
And rivers have a russet sedge,
   And great green elms one yellow bough;

I know the woods are full of glory,
   And smoky with wild clematis—
I know it, as I know a story
   Read in another year than this.

The Spendthrift

Out of your treasury, dear year,
You squander your last blue and gold.
Your summer held no days more clear
Although they had no tang of cold.
Sweet is the air with which you've swept
The withered leaf along the road;
You have a richer sunset kept
Than any May or August showed.
Unstintingly you spend your store
And fling bright day upon bright day
Until you are stripped bare once more,
And to the end must beg your way.

The Great Discovery
(*12 October, Columbus Day*)

Christofero had a mind
Facts were powerless to bind.

He declared that he had seen
Mermaids sporting on the green,

And the world, he used to swear,
Was not an orange, but a pear.

Little wonder then that he,
Blown across the unknown sea

On the quest of far Cathay,
Lit upon the U.S.A.,

And while seeking for the Khan
Met his first Red Indian.

Followers of the Sun

And whither, black-eyed gypsies,
  Oh whither do you go
When summer's past to 'scape the blast
  And shelter from the snow?
So sure as swallows vanish
  The way the sunbeams run,
So sure the crew of gypsies too
  Goes following the sun.

Oh is it back to Egypt
  Or back to Hindustan,

To some dim age in history's page
   They drive their caravan?
Where do they spell their fortunes
   When summer is outrun?
Where do the black-eyed tribes go back,
   The dwellers in the sun?

They'll never tell their secret,
   Never, to such as I!
For my demand they'll have at hand
   Some quick and pretty lie.
But sure as spring brings cuckoos
   Where winter brought us none,
The black-eyed train will come again
   Following the sun.

After Harvest

Now the last apple
Trembles on the bough,
The spider's grey silk
Spreads its jewels now.

Fields have been gleaned,
The stubble stands un-eared,
Spring's joyous traveller
Grows his winter beard.

Woolly mists
On midnight meadows creep,
And earth lies chilled
In after-harvest sleep.

Spinners in the Sun

They spin for life that is their need,
They spin for life that looks like greed,
    They are unconscious as they spin
    Of the stuff they labour in,
Save as it serves dear life to feed.

In the autumnal air their nets
They hang, and as September wets
    The web with dew, or shines in it
    Until the film with light is lit,
The eye that looks on it forgets

The reason why the work began;
The wondering eye of child and man
    Sees only that the spinners' pains
    Caught beauty in its filmy chains.
The spiders knew not what they span.

'Punkie-Night'
(A Somersetshire Custom on 30 October)

Here come children
On Punkie-night
With mangold-lanterns,
And candle-light
Gleaming inside
The goblin-faces'

Yellowy grins
And gold grimaces.
In and out
Of Hinton St George,
By church and hostel,
By farm and forge,
Swinging their gargoyle
Mangolds bright,
There go children
On Punkie-night.

Hallowe'en

On Hallowe'en the old ghosts come
About us, and they speak to some;
To others they are dumb.

They haunt the hearts that loved them best;
In some they are by grief possessed,
In other hearts they rest.

They have a knowledge they would tell;
To some of us it is a knell,
To some, a miracle.

They come unseen and go unseen;
And some will never know they've been,
And some know all they mean.

Sagittarius
(*A Zodiac Song*)

The Archer draws his bow,
  Oh he draws his windy bow,
His starry-pointed arrows
  Shooting high, shooting low:
But none can find a feather
  Of the shafts he lets fly,
For the wild windy weather
  Whirls them low, whirls them high.

Enter November

Here's November,
The year's sad daughter,
A loverless maid,
A lamb for the slaughter,
An empty mirror,
A sunless morn,
A withered wreath,
The husk of the corn,
A night that falls
Without a tomorrow,
Here's November,
The month of sorrow.

November's Song

I restore the primal line,
Stark and sturdy, frail and fine,
Of the Dryads in the sun.

Stripped to bone, in ranks they stand
With their root-grip on the land,
   Ghost no more, but skeleton.
Banks are thick with blackened mast,
Earth's redundancy is past.
   Let her rest. Her work is done.

Oliver Goldsmith
(Born 10 November 1728)

Oliver Goldsmith
Was careless and willing,
He'd write a sweet ballad
To sell for a shilling,
His wisdom was folly,
His labour was play,
He'd borrow a guinea
And give it away.

At school he was simple,
At college a dunce;
To earn bread-and-butter
He failed more than once;
So he whistled his way
Over many a land,
A hole in his pocket,
A flute in his hand.

In bloom-coloured breeches
And blue silken coat,
Tho' he talked like 'Poor Poll',
Like an angel he wrote;

The burst of an earthquake
Alarmed not his ears,
But the crack of a teacup
Reduced him to tears.

Oliver Goldsmith,
The day that he died
Samuel Johnson's
Stout heart-strings were tried;
'Poor Goldy!' said Garrick;
'Poor Goldy!' sighed Burke;
And Joshua Reynolds
Laid down his work.

Let rich men envy
The fellow who ends
Loved by his neighbours
And wept by his friends,
Like Oliver Goldsmith,
Careless and willing,
Whose life was a ballad
He sold for a shilling.

Memorial Garden (Canterbury)
(On Armistice Day)

The grey cathedral towers
Rise up like solid dreams
Above the garth where flowers
The late rose on the wall,
And yellow fruit-leaves fall.

Upon the leaded panes
Of the great window there
Many a little square
Of flattened light gleams out
As though new-set with rains.

And in the air about
The dreaming towers, the crows
Like loose dark leaves are blown
By the same wind that blows
The petals of the rose.

Summer and warmth are flown,
Life falls from tree and sky,
And still the grey dream stays,
The life of other days
That never will blow by.

And where the petals fall
In that Memorial
Garth to the Kentish dead,
Love will walk the ways
When the last leaf is shed.

Now! Says Time

Now! says Time,
and lifts his finger,
and the leaf on the lime
may not linger.

When Time utters
Now! and lifts
his finger, the oakleaf flutters
and drifts,
and elm and beech
let a leaf from the bough
when, finger lifted, to each
Time says *Now!*

The Trees and the Wind

Now every breath of air
    Brings down a leaf or so,
    No greedy wind doth blow
But carries off his share;
He has no mind to spare
    One leaf that clings and lingers.
Though trees, in poverty grown grim
To feed his idle wanton whim,
Stretch out their naked arms to him
    With crooked, pleading fingers.

The wind will take them all,
    The red, the brown, the gold,
    More than his hands can hold;
And still he makes his call,
And still the trees let fall
    All that he will not spare them—
Yet by the secrets of their roots
They know the strength that in them shoots,
Whose fruits shall one day be their fruits
    Alone that toiled to bear them.

To an Oak Dropping Acorns

With my two arms I cannot span thy girth,
Yet when I pick thy acorn from the earth
Within my hand I hold a ship at sea,
My bed, my table, and my own roof-tree.

The Old Man Sweeps the Leaves

The Old Man sweeps the leaves
Fallen everywhere
Through the soft cool air.
Each shake of wind bereaves
Some bough, and leaves it bare.

The gutters of old eaves
Are clogged with them, the feet
Of passers in the street
Shuffle the rustling sheaves
To chatter shrill and sweet.

The earth her own receives,
The layered hordes have flowed
Thick on the woodland road,
And time the burden weaves
Into one matted load.

And children go to school,
And none of them believes
In the bare tree, or grieves
To see how in the cool
The Old Man sweeps the leaves.

A Bag of Chestnuts

The chestnut man is in the street
With his glowing cave of heat.
He makes my hurrying footstep lag,
And takes my twopence for a bag.

Once more into the London cold
I turn my face. But as I hold
The hot brown nuts between my hands,
My heart is gone to other lands.

Were these the English squirrel's food?
Did they come from Rewel Wood,
Or any other wood that crowns
Some high curve of the Sussex Downs?

Or does the tree that bore them bear
The velvet-eyed Italian's fare,
And swelled they in the light that shines
On peasants in the Apennines?

I do not know: but I shall know
As soon as I dip in, and go
Tasting beneath the London sky
My England or my Italy.

Catherinette

(On 25 November, St Catherine's Day, in Paris unmarried girls over a certain age are said to be 'Capped by St Catherine'. These 'Catherinettes' wear demure lace caps as they walk in the streets.)

Catherinette,
Who never has yet
Been married or kissed,
Think what you've missed!

Crown your sweet face
With a bonnet of lace,
And walk in the city
So prim and so pretty.

Then some laughing lad
Will say 'It's too bad
Nobody's led her
To altar and wed her'—

And before you can speak,
He'll kiss your fair cheek
For fancy or fun,
And if you don't run,

Or tremble or faint,
The cap of the Saint
You may soon lay aside
For the veil of the bride.

Autumn Sigheth

Wind bloweth,
Water floweth
Feather flieth,
Bird goeth.
Whither, bird?
Who can tell?
None knoweth. . . .
Farewell.

Wind bawleth,
Summer palleth,
Rose fadeth,
Leaf falleth.
Wither, leaf,
Where you fell,
Winter calleth. . . .
Farewell.

Tree turneth,
Bonfire burneth,
Earth resteth,
Sleep earneth.
Whither, earth?
To dream a spell
Till flower returneth. . . .
Sleep well.

At Eventide

When the day has ended,
Do not sleep, oh do not sleep
Till your prayers have tended
All who laugh and all who weep.

Let your prayers like swallows
Eastward roam and westward roam,
Then, before sleep follows,
Bring them home, oh bring them home.

Flying all together,
Or alone, oh flying lone,
They will drop a feather
On the known and the unknown.

When your love has tended
All who laugh and all who weep,
And your prayers are ended,
Fall asleep, oh fall asleep.

Capricorn
(A Zodiac Song)

Capricorn, Capricorn
Bears December on his horn.
In the year's declining days
He has no green thing to graze.
He must drink of snow, and eat
Of ice, and men will hear him bleat
Munching at the frosty boughs
Round about the darkened house.

He will stare with agate eyes
At the empty earth and skies,
Wondering why he must bear
Scapegoat's portion of the year.
Till one night before one morn,
    Tired and torn,
    Patience worn,
Capricorn, Capricorn
Will toss December from his horn.

Three Miles to Penn

Today I walked three miles to Penn
With an uneasy mind.
The sun shone like a frozen eye,
A light that had gone blind.
The glassy air between the sky
And earth was frozen wind—
All motion and all light again
Were closed within a rind,
As I by wood and field to Penn
Took trouble in my mind.

The slopes of cloud in heaven that lay,
Unpeopled hills grown old,
Had no more movement than the land
Locked in a flowing mould;
The sheep like mounds of cloudy sand
Stood soundless in the cold;
There was no stir on all the way
Save what my heart did hold,
So quiet earth and heaven lay,
So quiet and so old.

By Dippel Woods

I knew no woman, child, or man
Had been before my steps today.
By Dippel Woods the snow-lanes ran
Soft and uncrushed above their clay;
But little starry feet had traced
Their passages as though in words,
And all those lanes of snow were laced
With runnings of departed birds.

Advice to a Child

Set your fir-tree
In a pot;
Needles green
Is all it's got.
Shut the door
And go away,
And so to sleep
Till Christmas Day.
In the morning
Seek your tree,
And you shall see
What you shall see.

Hang your stocking
By the fire,
Empty of
Your heart's desire;

Up the chimney
Say your say,
And so to sleep
Till Christmas Day.
In the morning
Draw the blind,
And you shall find
What you shall find.

Christmas Stocking

What will go into the Christmas Stocking
While the clock on the mantelpiece goes tick-tocking?
    An orange, a penny,
    Some sweets, not too many,
    A trumpet, a dolly,
    A sprig of red holly,
    A book and a top
    And a grocery shop,
    Some beads in a box,
    An ass and an ox
    And a lamb, plain and good,
    All whittled in wood,
    A white sugar dove,
    A handful of love,
    Another of fun,
    And it's very near done—
    A big silver star
    On top—there you are!
Come morning you'll wake to the clock's tick-tocking,
And that's what you'll find in the Christmas Stocking.

The Princesses' Carol

Elizabeth of Hungary
Who wore a golden crown
Loaves for the poor ones
Carried in her gown.
Once when she went
Their hunger to fulfill
The loaves were changed to roses
By heaven's will.

 Sweet Saint Elizabeth,
 Let your rose light
 On all young Elizabeths
 Come Christmas Night.

Margaret of Scotland
Who wore a golden dress
Looked to the little ones
In loneliness.
Nine small orphans
Daily ere noon
She fed on her knees
From a porridge-spoon.

 Dear Saint Margaret,
 Let your love stay
 By all small Margarets
 Come Christmas Day.

The Sands

The sands are running out, old Time,
The sands are running thin,
Oh, turn the glass about, about,
And let the young time in.

The sands are soon to pass, old Time,
The sands are running through,
Oh, turn the glass, oh, turn the glass
And let old sands run new.

Up the Hill, Down the Hill

Old One, lie down,
Your journey is done,
Little New Year
Will rise with the sun.
Now you have come to
The foot of the hill,
Lay down your bones,
Old Year, and lie still.

Young One, step out,
Your journey's begun,
Weary Old Year
Makes way for his son.
Now you have started
To climb up the hill,
Put best foot forward,
New Year, with a will.

Up the hill, down the hill,
Which is the best?
Up-hill is labour,
And down-hill is rest.

The Moon upon her Watch-tower

The moon upon her watch-tower
With her golden eye
Guarded the quarters
East and West the sky.
Just as midnight
Was stepping past
One drew his first breath,
One drew his last.
The moon upon her watch-tower
Rang a soundless bell—
It might have been for welcome,
It might have been farewell.

A Burying

I see the twelve fair months go by
Bearing a coffin shoulder-high.
What, laughing? Pretty pall-bearers,
Pitiless of the buried years,
Have ye never a tear to shed
Nor sigh to drop for the newly-dead,
Nor marble grief to mark his grave?—
No, none of these; but see, we have
Green seed to mingle with his earth.—
What, is not this a burying?—Nay, a birth.

Index of Titles